COLLINS

Design and Technology
Food
Foundation Course

Sue Plews
Head of Technology Faculty
Walton Girls High School, Grantham

Janet Inglis
Head of Design and Technology
Hanson School, Bradford

Eileen Chapman
Associate Deputy Head (Curriculum)
William Farr C of E Comprehensive School, Welton

CollinsEducational
An imprint of HarperCollinsPublishers

|CONTENTS

Published by Collins Educational
An imprint of HarperCollinsPublishers Ltd
77–85 Fulham Palace Road
London W6 8JB

The HarperCollins website is www.**fire**and**water**.com

First published 1999

ISBN 000 329 4919

British Library Cataloguing in Publication Data
A catalogue record for this book is available from the British Library.

Designed by Ken Vail Graphic Design
Cover Design by Ken Vail Graphic Design
Cover photograph: Angus Mill and Gerber Ltd
Illustrated by: Nick Hawken, Simon Girling Artists Agency (Mike Lacey and
Peter Wilks), Ross Thomson and Ken Vail Graphic Design
Commissioned by: Alison Walters
Edited by: Lesley Young
Editorial Assistant: Tamsin Miller
Production: Anna Pauletti
Printed and bound by Scotprint

WHAT IS FOOD TECHNOLOGY?

Design and Technology (D&T) is an exciting subject where you can design and make products in different materials. This book looks at how to design and make food products.

Through D&T you will be asked to use your knowledge of maths and science to help you design products. IT skills are also very important and you will be encouraged to use these skills wherever necessary.

As you progress through school you will probably be offered the opportunity to take one of the options in D&T at examination level. The diagram on the right shows how you can follow your chosen D&T option through school and onto higher education if you wish. Alternatively you may decide to go straight from school to work.

Food technology can lead to exciting and well-paid opportunities in the food industry. The following are just some of the possible careers in the food industry:

- Designer, designing new food products;
- Home economist, testing new food products;
- Quality controller, responsible for the final quality of all the products made in the processing plant. This includes planning and which quality control tests will be carried out;
- Buyer, sourcing ingredients from all over the world;
- Production manager, responsible for the running of the processing plant where food is manufactured.

The food industry is important, as the largest of our industries it provides jobs and creates wealth for the nation.

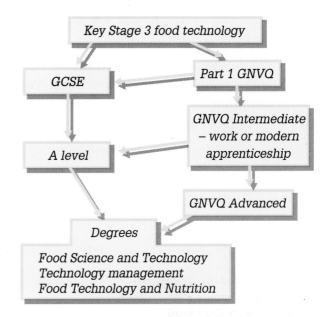

Key Stage 3 food technology
GCSE
Part 1 GNVQ
GNVQ Intermediate – work or modern apprenticeship
A level
GNVQ Advanced
Degrees
Food Science and Technology
Technology management
Food Technology and Nutrition

Food technology is also valuable outside the food industry. It will help you to develop an understanding of nutrition and healthy eating. These may be important if you want to work in medicine or in the caring professions such as nursery nursing or working in homes for the elderly.

Whatever area you work in when you leave school, food technology will help you to develop valuable skills, of organisation and communication.

1 DESIGNING

The process of designing and making a product can be divided into groups of activities. The diagram shown in Fig. 1.1 shows the design process and the stages involved in it. In order to make it easier to understand, the process is shown as a line, but in fact it is more like the circular process shown in Fig. 1.2. For instance, once you have made something and evaluated it, you could go through the whole process again and improve your design. On the other hand, you may begin designing by evaluating something which has already been made by you or someone else.

1 Starting points
Contexts
Identifying needs
Design briefs
Evaluating existing products

2 Generating a design proposal
Drawing up a specification
Sketching and modelling
Ideas
Evaluating ideas
Choosing ideas

3 Planning and making
Product planning
Resource planning
Action planning
Making

4 Evaluating
Final evaluation
Other people's evaluation
Improving your finished product

Fig. 1.1
A linear design process

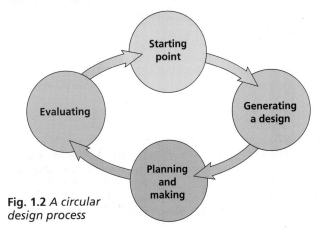

Fig. 1.2 *A circular design process*

Design frameworks

At first, designing might seem to be a complicated activity with many different things to think about, but designing products is not difficult if you know what to do. If you were sent on an errand to a place that you had not been to before, you would probably be given a map with a route marked on it. In D&T you can use a series of design frameworks as a route through the process of designing. These frameworks will help you to design and make quality products. Design frameworks will guide you through the development of your product. When you first begin designing and making products, the design frameworks should give you a lot of help. As you develop your designing skills, however, you will be able to do more of the work yourself. Gradually you will take control of your work and eventually the design framework will be made up of just a series of headings for each part of the project. Fig. 1.3 shows an example of a framework. You can see that a lot of the work has already been done for you.

Context
Vegetarian students eating lunch in the school canteen have very few choices of snack food. The food available is predictable and dull. Investigate a healthy vegetarian option, which would appeal to students. Use your investigation to develop a product which you could present to the canteen manager.

Brief
A brief is a statement which tells other people what you are going to do.
Complete the following brief:
I am going to design and make...

Analysis
Finding out more about what you have to do is known as analysing the situation.
Answer the following questions in full sentences.
1 How much time will you have to make and evaluate your snack product?
2 Which different types of snack food will appeal to students?
3 Which ingredients could be used for the product?
4 How much will it cost to make?
5 Do I need to use any special ingredients?
6 Is there anything else I need to know in order to finish this work?

| Name | Form | D&T Teacher |

Fig. 1.3 *A design framework*

Starting points

There are several ways of starting to design things. These starting points will change as your designing skills develop.

Design briefs ➡

You may be given a brief which will tell you what you have to design and make. You will need to think carefully about the brief and try to work out exactly what is required. Professional designers often work in this way when they are given a brief by their customer or client. The final product is agreed, but its final shape, colour and flavour may be left for the designer to decide. Sometimes the brief will ask you to design and make a new product to fit into an existing range, or it may ask you to design a product for a particular group of people such as children or vegetarians.

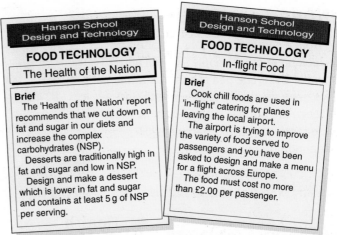

Hanson School Design and Technology
FOOD TECHNOLOGY
The Health of the Nation

Brief
The 'Health of the Nation' report recommends that we cut down on fat and sugar in our diets and increase the complex carbohydrates (NSP).
Desserts are traditionally high in fat and sugar and low in NSP.
Design and make a dessert which is lower in fat and sugar and contains at least 5 g of NSP per serving.

Hanson School Design and Technology
FOOD TECHNOLOGY
In-flight Food

Brief
Cook chill foods are used in 'in-flight' catering for planes leaving the local airport.
The airport is trying to improve the variety of food served to passengers and you have been asked to design and make a menu for a flight across Europe.
The food must cost no more than £2.00 per passenger.

Fig. 1.4 *Design briefs*

Fig. 1.5 *Design and make a new dessert which is low in sugar, but high in dietary fibre*

Contexts

You may be given a context or situation to work from. You will be expected to investigate the context, work out what is required and write your own design brief. The context will describe a particular situation for you to think about. You may, for example, consider the variety of the food served in the school canteen. This would allow you to look at the different needs of people eating in the canteen, their likes and dislikes, the cost of school meals, the nutritional value of the meals and the problem of litter if food is taken out of the canteen. This would provide you with a range of opportunities from which you could select one area to write a design brief. Your brief might look like this:

Fig. 1.6 *'I am going to design and make a new dish which would appeal to students who are vegetarian. The product must be suitable to eat with the hands and must cost no more than the other meals served in the canteen.'*

Identifying needs ➡

Working from a context or a situation often involves looking at other people's needs and requirements. Everyone has needs – as human beings we need air, water, food, warmth and shelter. These are our basic needs, but in addition to these we have other needs or wants, depending upon our situation.

Fig. 1.7 *Food is a basic need*

⬅ Health

People with certain illnesses may have special dietary needs. For example, diabetics need food which contains little or no refined sugar. People with heart disease may need to eat a diet which is low in fats. Other people may be trying to eat a healthier diet which includes more fruits and vegetables.

Fig 1.8

Religion

Different religions may have dietary rules about what may or may not be eaten. **Muslim** food should be halal. This means that meat must come from animals which were slaughtered according to Muslim law. Pork, fish without scales, shellfish and alcohol are all forbidden foods for Muslims.

Buddhists are often vegetarian as Buddhism preaches against killing. However, they are not forbidden to eat meat and they may eat fish.

Hindus may not drink alcohol and are forbidden to eat beef because the cow is a sacred animal to Hindus. They may, however, eat other meats.

Jewish food should be Kosher, that is, meat must come from an animal which has been blessed and slaughtered in a particular way according to Jewish law. Pork, fish without scales, shellfish, eels and birds of prey are also forbidden in Jewish diets.

Fig. 1.9 *Kosher food*

Culture

Many nations have their own cultural views about food. In parts of Europe, for example, it is normal to eat horse meat, while in Britain this is uncommon. In other parts of the world people eat snake flesh, beetles or grubs – an idea which we might find unpleasant

Fig. 1.10 *Preparing a witchity grub to eat*

Some people become vegetarians or vegans because of their own beliefs and values. Vegetarians will not eat meat or fish, while vegans will not eat fish, meat or any animal products such as eggs or milk.

As a food designer you will need to consider the people who will be eating your product. They may have particular needs or wants which your product will have to meet.

Fig. 1.11 *Foods suitable for vegetarians often carry a symbol showing that they are approved by the Vegetarian Society*

Investigate the dietary laws of a religion other than your own.

Evaluating existing products

Working from existing products is another way to start designing. This involves looking very closely at products, finding out what they are made from, how they are made, whether or not they harm the environment, how safe they are and whether or not people like them. If you think carefully you should be able to work out what the original needs were. Then you can check if they are being met by the product.

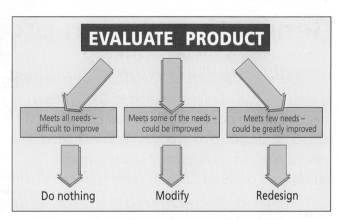

EVALUATE PRODUCT

Meets all needs – difficult to improve

Meets some of the needs – could be improved

Meets few needs – could be greatly improved

Do nothing   Modify   Redesign

Fig. 1.12

You will need to consider if it would be possible to improve the design of the product or the way in which it is made. This is known as **evaluating existing products** or **product analysis**. Many new food products are the result of redesigning existing products. (See page 27.)

Part of evaluating existing products includes **disassembly**. In food work we disassemble products by identifying the ingredients used to make them and working out why each ingredient is in the product.

Fig. 1.13 *A beefburger is made of minced beef (protein), egg to bind the minced beef, breadcrumbs to coat the burger, and salt as a flavour enhancer*

From this point you can consider other ingredients which could be used to make the product. This is a starting point for new product designs.

By taking one example from each column you will be starting to make new design proposals (for example, Quorn, flavoured with chopped mint, mixed with cream and coated in nuts, or lamb flavoured with grated onion, mixed with egg and coated in wholemeal breadcrumbs. Some of these new ideas will not be very appealing; but others will sound interesting. You may need to carry out some market research to find out which ideas are most likely to succeed.

Protein	Binding	Coating	Flavouring	Flavour enhancer
chicken	egg	egg and flour	mixed herbs	salt
fish	cream	chopped nuts	chopped mint	lo-salt
lentils	water	wholemeal breadcrumbs	grated onion	
Quorn	milk	breadcrumbs with herbs	garlic	
lamb	egg and water	cheese and breadcrumbs	diced pepper	
cheese		flour		

Consumer pull, technology push ➡

Food products are sometimes made because consumers have asked for products to meet their own particular needs. This is known as **consumer pull**. One example of this is the rise in demand for meals for one now that more people than ever live alone.

The food industry also often produces new food products when new equipment becomes available. This could be equipment for storing or cooking food in the home, like microwave ovens and freezers or it may be new equipment used in the food industry, such as extruders. This is known as **technology push**.

Fig. 1.14 *Microwave ovens are a result of technology push*

Disassemble a product which you enjoy eating, such as pizza, chicken nuggets or fish fingers. Design three new products based on this food.

Generating design proposals

Looking very carefully at something or studying it in detail is called investigation in D&T. This means finding out as much as you can about a situation, problem or product. You will need to investigate the design brief or the context carefully in order to find out what you need to do.

Fig. 1.15

Investigating will involve many different skills and sources of information. Try to use as wide a variety of sources as you can.

Talking to people or making observations yourself is known as gathering **primary** information. Using books or information gathered by other people is called **secondary** information. You should use both primary and secondary sources of information for your investigations.

Market research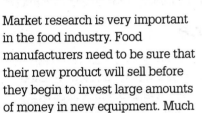

Market research is very important in the food industry. Food manufacturers need to be sure that their new product will sell before they begin to invest large amounts of money in new equipment. Much of the machinery used in the food industry is very specialised and can cost thousands of pounds to build.

A useful way of gathering primary information is by going to look at products already available on the market, that are in shops, supermarkets, restaurants, takeaway outlets, cafes, etc. You can also gather primary information by talking to people. This may be done through interviews or by using a questionnaire. You may have access to a computer program which will help you to write a questionnaire and then allow you to make graphs from the information you have gathered.

Before you begin to write your questionnaire, decide on the following points:
- What do I want to find out? – Keep to the point and only ask questions about this.

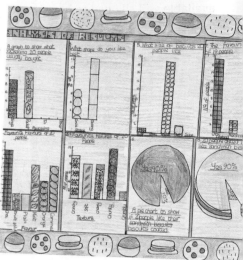

Fig 1.16 *Try to present your work in an interesting way*

- Who will I ask? – If your product is to be designed for teenagers, don't ask adults!
- How will I record the answers? – Will you use a tape recorder, tally chart or individual questionnaires to fill in?
- And remember – BE POLITE!

To write a successful questionnaire you need to use different styles of questions. There are three basic types of questions and you will need to decide which type will give you the answers you need. The following are examples of the types of questions you might ask if you were trying to find out people's likes and dislikes about chocolate biscuits.

- **Closed questions** are questions from which you will get a 'yes' or 'no' answer, e.g. 'Do you like chocolate biscuits?'
- **Open questions** will help you to get a wide variety of information from people, but you need to be careful as sometimes this type of answer will not help you to make

design proposals. An example of an open question would be 'What kind of chocolate biscuits do you like?'
- **Multiple choice questions** give the person answering the question a number of choices. This will help you to collect information which you can use in your designing. For example:

Which do you prefer?	
chocolate and orange	☐
chocolate and coffee	☐
chocolate and mint	☐
chocolate and toffee	☐
chocolate and banana	☐
chocolate and chocolate chip	☐

Write a questionnaire to be used to discover the types of desserts people prefer to eat in the summer. Try to do this on a computer if you have access to one.

Design specifications

Constraints ➡

When you are carrying out your investigations it is important to think about all the things that may affect your product. The amount of time you have to work in, your own skills and the money available will all need to be considered before you draw up a specification for your product. These things are called **constraints** and they will have an important effect on your work. Sometimes the constraints are written into the brief by the client.

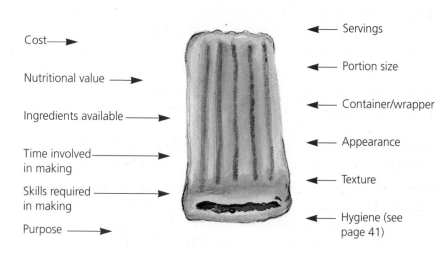

Cost ➡
Nutritional value ➡
Ingredients available ➡
Time involved in making ➡
Skills required in making ➡
Purpose ➡

⬅ Servings
⬅ Portion size
⬅ Container/wrapper
⬅ Appearance
⬅ Texture
⬅ Hygiene (see page 41)

Fig 1.17 *The constraints on the design of a biscuit*

Fig. 1.18 *A simple specification*

My biscuit design for the school canteen should:
• cost a similar amount to other biscuits which are on sale in the canteen
• be low in sugar
• be high in dietary fibre (NSP)
• be hygienically made
• be made in one lesson

Fig. 1.19 *A detailed specification*

Essential criteria – My biscuit design for the school canteen must:
• cost a similar amount to other biscuits which are on sale in the canteen
• be high in dietary fibre (NSP)
• be hygienically made
• be made in one lesson
• cost no more than 15p per biscuit
• be attractive to teenagers
• be between 2 and 3cm in diameter
• be made by the rubbed in method

Desirable criteria – My biscuit design for the school canteen should:
• be fruit flavoured
• be decorated
• be low in sugar

⬅ Criteria

Criteria are important targets that you want your product to meet. When you have worked out the criteria that your product must meet, you should make a list of them. This forms the **design specification**. You may write a simple specification which lists the criteria in any order of importance. Alternatively, you may write a more detailed specification which will divide the criteria into two groups: essential and desirable.

Essential criteria are the things your product **must** do. **Desirable** criteria are the criteria your product **should** meet if possible.

Specifications are an important part of designing. They provide a checklist which you can test your ideas against. If you write a detailed specification, you will find it easier to evaluate and develop your ideas. The number of decisions you will have to make will be limited as the specification will guide you. Specifications will also help you to evaluate the finished product to show that you have been successful in designing and making what you were asked to.

Choose a product which you enjoy eating. Write a specification for this product.

Presenting information

Some of the information you have collected may be presented as text. Other information will need to be presented graphically, using **bar charts, pie charts, pictographs** or **pictures**. All charts should have a title and the axes must be labelled.

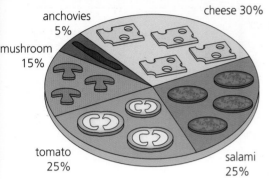

Fig. 1.20 *A 'pizza' pie chart*

Pie charts

Pie charts are easy to understand and can be very colourful and interesting. The 'pie' may be drawn to represent the food you are investigating, such as pizza or cake. Pie charts are most suitable when you have a complete set of results and you want to show how individual results compare with one another. To make a pie chart, draw a circle and divide it into sections. Each section must be carefully measured and labelled. Remember that 3.6° of the circle = 1%. Spread sheet programs will allow you to create pie charts.

Bar charts ➡

Bar charts like the one in Fig. 1.21 are another way of presenting your information. The bars on the chart should always have a space between them like the ones in the drawing. Spread sheet programs will also create bar charts.

Fig. 1.21

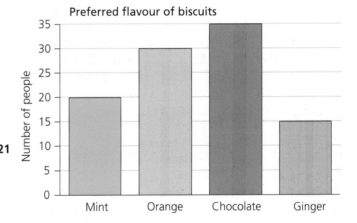

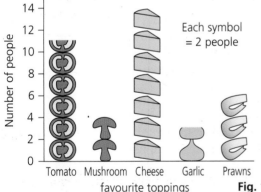

Fig. 1.22 *Favourite pizza toppings*

Pictographs

Pictographs are an attractive way of presenting data. The symbols can be drawn or if you are not very good at drawing you could use your computer to generate the symbols.

Fig. 1.23 *Graphs from a spreadsheet have been dropped into a word processing package*

Text and pictures ➡

Text and pictures may be put together using a desk-top publishing or work-processing package. Graphs, digital images from a camera or scanner and text can be combined. These applications have the benefit of checking your spelling before you print. They can also be changed easily if you need to alter your work.

Use the information you gathered in the questionnaire on desserts (page 10). Present the results as a bar chart. Try to use a computer for this.

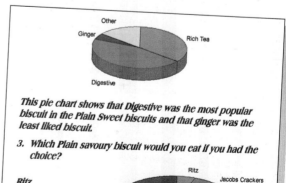

Ideas

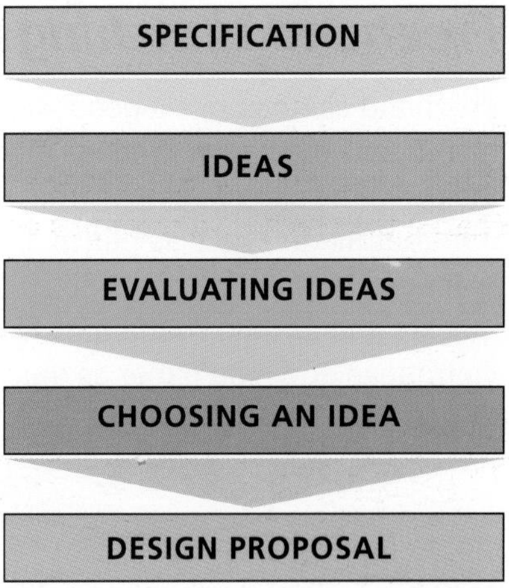

Once you have drawn up a specification, the next stage in generating a design proposal is to start thinking about ideas or solutions to the design brief. The aim is to begin with a number of ideas and develop one of them into a design proposal. Fig. 1.24 shows these stages in the design process.

SPECIFICATION

IDEAS

EVALUATING IDEAS

CHOOSING AN IDEA

DESIGN PROPOSAL

Fig. 1.24

Use your specification

Don't worry if you do not feel inspired! The specification will help you because it provides you with a detailed list of the criteria your product must satisfy. At this stage just try to produce as many ideas as you can. Try to be creative as even the silliest ideas may be of use later. The concept of low-fat biscuits was probably thought very unlikely at first, but now we can buy these in many shops. Remember to compare your ideas with the specification as you work, checking that they will satisfy the criteria you have decided are important.

Ideas are quickly forgotten if you do not record them. It is possible to make a note of your ideas but you will probably find it quicker and easier to draw them. If you are using a book for inspiration, you may decide to photocopy the pictures, or you can use illustrations from magazines. Scanning images or using a digital camera to take photographs are alternative ways of recording ideas based on existing products.

Low fat orange

High fibre

Biscuits

Coffee and walnut cream

Mint and chocolate bar

Chocolate and orange cream

Fig. 1.25

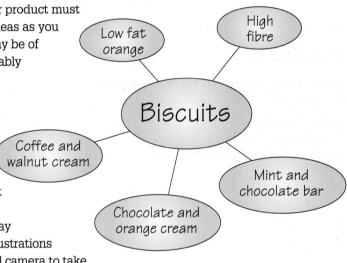

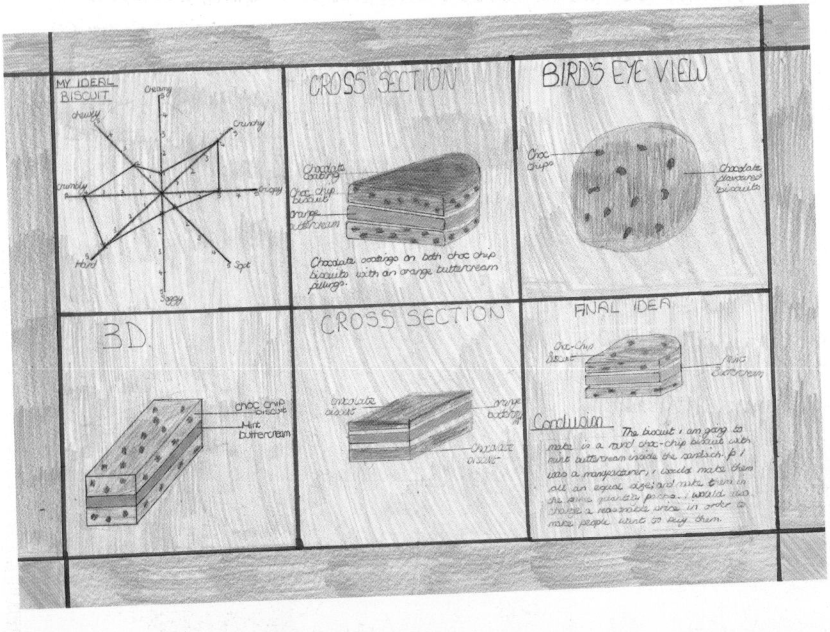

Whatever method you choose, your work must be easy to understand and well presented so that other people will be able to grasp the ideas you are trying to communicate.

Fig. 1.26 *Ideas recorded by students*

Freehand sketching ➡

Freehand sketching is a good way to record and present your ideas quickly. Ideas can be sketched in a variety of different media, such as pencil, ball-point pen or fine-line pen. Sketch quickly and lightly. Your aim is to get your ideas down on paper as quickly as you can.

Giant orange and chocolate chip biscuit

Small shaped biscuits

Biscuits in letter shapes

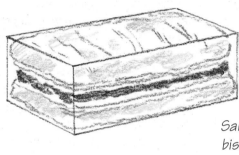

Sandwich wafer biscuit in crate

Fig. 1.27

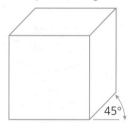

Oblique drawing

Isometric drawing

45°

30°   30°

Fig. 1.28 *Oblique and isometric drawings can be used to draw crated objects*

⬅ Sketching in 3D

Some ideas in Fig. 1.27 have been drawn in two dimensions (2D) and others in three dimensions (3D). Two-dimensional drawings show only two basic measurements (dimensions) – height and width. A three-dimensional drawing shows three basic measurements – height, width and depth. Three-dimensional drawings show more information and make your ideas look more realistic than two-dimensional drawings.

It is sometimes helpful to draw a 3D box and draw an object inside it, using the box as a guide. This is known as **crating**. As you become more experienced you will find that you can draw objects in 3D without using crates.

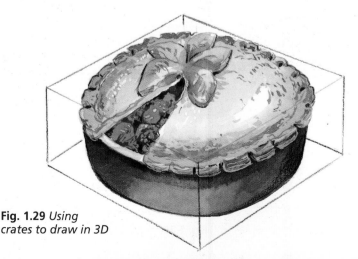

Fig. 1.29 *Using crates to draw in 3D*

Practise drawing 3D diagrams of food products. You could include the following: a can of Coca-Cola, a packet of biscuits, a cake, a burger. Start by using a crate to help you.

Evaluating ideas

When you evaluate ideas, you choose the most suitable idea to develop further. Evaluating is a very important stage in the design process. Careful evaluation will ensure that your design meets the criteria set out in the specification. If you do not evaluate your work carefully, it is very easy to stray away from the topic and design things which do not really meet the criteria.

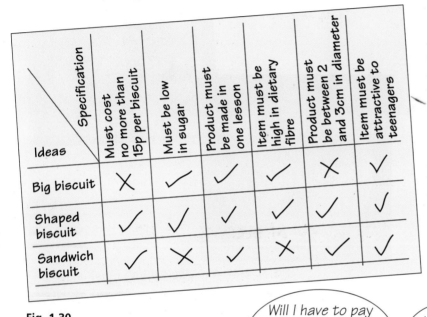

Ideas \ Specification	Must cost no more than 15p per biscuit	Must be low in sugar	Product must be made in one lesson	Item must be high in dietary fibre	Product must be between 2 and 3cm in diameter	Item must be attractive to teenagers
Big biscuit	✗	✓	✓	✓	✗	✓
Shaped biscuit	✓	✓	✓	✓	✓	✓
Sandwich biscuit	✓	✗	✓	✗	✓	✓

Fig. 1.30

A simple way of beginning an evaluation of your ideas is to make a checklist like the one in **Fig. 1.30**, with your ideas across the top and the criteria from the specification down the side. Look at each idea in turn. If it agrees with the criteria, tick the box; if it doesn't, put a cross in the box. This way you will be able to see which ideas are worth developing.

Choosing an idea ➡

When you have completed your checklist you must look very carefully at the ideas that satisfy the criteria of the specification. You will need to ask yourself a number of questions about the wider design considerations which may affect your work. Fig. 1.31 will give you some idea of the types of questions you may want to ask yourself. Sometimes you may feel that one idea is the best but it may, for example, be too expensive. At this stage you would have to **compromise** by deciding to develop the second-best idea which is less expensive.

When you have done this you will be able to choose one or more of your ideas for the design of your product. The chosen ideas are known as the **design proposal**.

Which of my ideas do I like the best?

Can my product be made hygienically?

Will I have to pay for the materials? Will my product be expensive to make?

How will I finance my product?

Will my product be environmentally friendy?

Have I the ability to make my product or will I need help from other people?

How will my product be served or sold?

Will my product look good?

How many portions will I be able to make?

Developing your chosen idea

Before you can begin to make your chosen idea several things still need to be considered. This stage is known as developing the chosen idea and it is a very important part of the design process.

Appearance ➡

The visual appearance of a product is very important. Designers aim to produce attractive products which suit the needs of people. The visual qualities which make things look attractive are known as **aesthetics**. Think about how you can make your food product look attractive. Pastry products may be glazed with beaten egg and water before cooking to give a shiny brown surface. Sweet products may look better if they are decorated, with glacé cherries for example. Savoury products may be garnished using parsley or tomato to give extra colour.

Fig. 1.32 *Which of these dishes would you prefer?*

Portion sizes ➡

You will need to decide how many portions, or servings, you will make from your recipe and how you will divide the mixture evenly. The portions may be made before the food is cooked (bread rolls, for example, are portioned and shaped before baking). These portions are often weighed to guarantee that they are equal.

Some products, such as cakes, are cut into portions after cooking and you will need to decide how you will do this evenly. Tools can be bought which will help you to do this easily and fairly.

Fig. 1.33 *Bread rolls being portioned before baking*

Fig. 1.34 *In industry portions are often measured electronically*

How big the portions will be will depend on the people you are serving. Young children will need much smaller portions than adolescent boys, for example. The cost of the ingredients may also help you to decide how big the portions will be.
Expensive foods are often served in smaller portions.

Make a list of the different techniques used to finish baked products like bread or pastry. Use a recipe book to find different ways of garnishing or decorating various dishes. Practise your graphic skills by drawing these. Look at Fig. 1.32. Which plate would most people prefer? Explain why this is more attractive.

16

Modelling

Modelling is an excellent way of developing your idea as it gives you a clear idea of what your finished product will look like. A model is anything which represents real objects and it may be 2D, 3D or mathematical. A designer will use a variety of models at different stages of designing. Modelling helps to solve problems before you begin using expensive materials. Most food products are modelled by making small quantities of the product.

Two-dimensional (2D) modelling

Drawings are one type of 2D modelling. They allow you to show how you want your product to look when it is completed. Drawings are inexpensive, allowing you to consider alternative types of finish, shape or ingredients without using real food.

There are a variety of drawing techniques which you may use in your design work. Some are quick, simple ways of recording ideas; others are more detailed, high quality drawings.

Annotated drawings ➡

It is often a good idea to add notes to your drawings as this can give more detail or record your thoughts as you are working. Drawings with notes added are known as annotated drawings.

Highlighting and **rendering** with colour can be used to make an object look more realistic. This is done by adding details which give an impression of the type of material being used and by adding highlights. Highlights give an impression of light falling on the object, creating shadows.

Presentation drawings are another form of 2D modelling. They are high quality representations used to make the product look as realistic as possible. The drawing is rendered in colour, using marker pens, coloured pencils or water-colour.

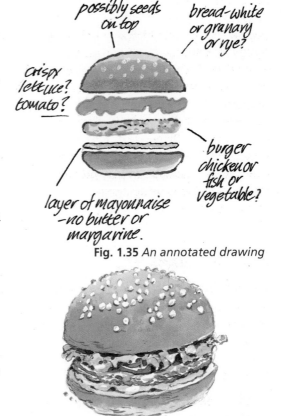

Fig. 1.35 *An annotated drawing*

Fig. 1. 36 *Using highlighting and rendering*

⬅ Perspective drawings

Two main types of perspective drawings are used in D&T – **single-point perspective** and **two-point perspective**. Two-point perspective is used more frequently as it allows us to draw items at an angle rather than straight on. This makes the objects look more realistic. Perspective drawing uses the fact that, to our eyes, the lines of objects going away into the distance appear to meet at a vanishing point somewhere on the horizon. Try standing at the end of a long corridor and look at the way the floor and ceiling appear to move closer together in the distance. Fig. 1. 37 shows how to draw a cube in two-point perspective.

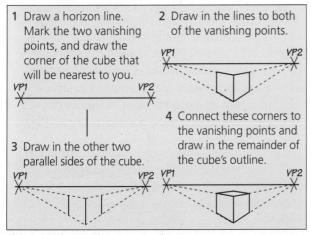

1 Draw a horizon line. Mark the two vanishing points, and draw the corner of the cube that will be nearest to you.

2 Draw in the lines to both of the vanishing points.

3 Draw in the other two parallel sides of the cube.

4 Connect these corners to the vanishing points and draw in the remainder of the cube's outline.

Fig. 1.37 *Two-point perspective*

Spreadsheets

Another form of 2D modelling is mathematical. This can be done quite quickly and simply using either a **spreadsheet** or a **database program**. This is a useful way of checking that your product meets the specification for nutritional quality or for cost before you begin trialing.

When designing food products you may be asked to lower the fat or sugar content or to increase the dietary fibre (NSP) in the product. You can model the amount of any nutrient in the product by using any spreadsheet or a database program made specially for dietary analysis.

	A	B	C	D	E	F	G
1	*Ingredients*	*Quantity (8)*	*per scone*	*12*	*50*	*144*	*kg*
2	S. R. Flour	200	25	.300	1250	3600	3.60
3	Margarine	50	6.25	75	312.5	900	0.90
4	Skimmed Milk	125	15.625	187.5	781.3	2250	2.25
5	Cheddar	30	3.75	45	187.5	540	0.54
6	Walnuts	10	1.25	15	62.5	180	0.18
7	Salt	2	0.25	3	12.5	36	0.04

Fig. 1.38 *Modelling on a computer*

Mathematical modelling using spreadsheets will allow you to:
- check costs;
- scale up ingredients;
- vary ingredients to show the effect on the nutritional quality;
- vary ingredients to show how the cost is altered;
- check portions;
- produce nutritional information for use on labels.

A large airline modelled the cost of the salads they served as the first course of their inflight meals. The salads each had three olives on top as a garnish. By reducing the number of olives to two the airline calculated that they could save $40,000 dollars (approximately £25,000) a year!

> Use a diet analysis program to work out the nutritional content of a product you have made.
> On a spreadsheet work out how much the product cost you. How much would it cost if you made 150 of the same product? How much would the overall cost be if you added a 25% profit margin?

Three-dimensional (3D) modelling

When designing with food you will need to model your ideas by making small samples of the dish and comparing how they look and taste.

In food manufacture small quantities of the food product are often made to test how the ingredients work together. These are usually tested by some form of sensory analysis (see page 19). By investigating how the **sensory characteristics**, **nutritional value** and the **physical properties change** when ingredients are altered you can decide which ingredients work well together to form new food products. These three areas, along with costings can help you to make informed decisions

Production lines

Modelling a production line using lego can help you to understand how sensors work in the food industry. The photograph to the right shows a lego conveyor belt attached to a motor. The sensor detects changes in the light. Burned or undercooked products reflect a different light value from those of

Fig. 1.39 *A lego model of a conveyor belt*

the perfectly cooked items. The sensor detects this change and feeds back the information to the computer. The computer is programmed to respond by stopping the conveyor belt while the robot arm moves across to remove the imperfect product. The conveyor belt then begins to move again. Sensors can be used to detect a wide variety of items in manufacturing, including weight, viscosity (thickness) of sauces, metal, pH value.

> Using the control equipment in school, try to set up a conveyor belt similar to the one above. Find out what sensors are available to you. Can you make a conveyor belt stop if the product is underweight or contains metal?

Trialing and testing

Once you have created your design proposal you will need to find recipes which you can use to make the products. You will need to think about the ingredients in the recipe and decide if these can be changed to improve the recipe in any way. Altering the ingredients is sometimes called **modifying** or **amending** a recipe. Before you can amend a recipe you need to understand how ingredients work together to make new products. Chapter 2 will help you to learn about ingredients.

To find out if it is possible to alter the ingredients in a recipe you may need to carry out some investigations. When experimenting, remember that you must make sure that the test is fair. Think about the way you conduct experiments in the science lab and then apply the same rules when modelling food products. Fig. 1.40 shows how three different design ideas were modelled. In this investigation the student wanted to find out if the cake mixture would be as popular if the NSP (dietary fibre) content was increased.

Basic recipe
50 g margarine   50 g caster sugar
1 egg size 3   50 g SR flour

Equipment?
Bowl
Sieve
Wooden spoon
Scales
Electric mixer
Bun cases

Method
Place all the ingredients in a bowl.
Mix with an electric mixer set on high for two minutes.
Divide evenly into 9 bun cases.
Cook for 12 minutes until risen and golden brown.

Appearance

Make three batches,
one with white self-raising flour
one with wholemeal self-raising flour
one with 25 g white self-raising flour and 25 g wholemeal self-raising flour

Taste

To make a fair test
Only change one variable (the flour).
Keep all the other ingredients the same.
Weigh all the ingredients accurately.
Use the same scales for weighing.
Mix for the same length of time – use a stop watch
Use an electric mixer to give the same power.
Use the same size container.
Cook at the same temperature.
Cook for the same length of time.
Cook at the same position in the oven.

Conclusion – which flour I will use and why.

Fig. 1.40

Sensory analysis

Tasting food to decide how much it is liked or if differences can be detected in different samples is known as **sensory analysis**. How much we enjoy food depends on what the food looks, smells, feels and tastes like. These are four of our five senses. We also respond to sound when enjoying food. Think about the sounds some foods make (buttering toast, frying bacon, cereals crackling when milk is added, opening a new bottle of fizzy drink) all of these sounds tell us something about what the food is like.

Once you have made new products you will want to find out what people think about them and how they could be improved. To do this you can set up a **taste panel** to conduct a sensory analysis of your product.

Fig. 1.41 *Taste testing*

■ Set up a quiet area where people will not be disturbed.
■ Give the tasters a drink of water to sip between samples.
■ Use small quantities of food with clean utensils each time.
■ Use codes or symbols for the products to prevent the tasters being influenced by the name of the product.
■ Do **NOT** allow people to put dirty spoons into your product.
■ Make sure that the tasters know how to fill in any charts you are using.

Sensory analysis can be organised in different ways, according to what you are trying to find out. **Preference testing**, including

ranking and rating tests, is used to find out which products people like best. **Comparative testing** is used to find out if people can detect differences in food products. Sensory analysis is also used to analyse the different attributes (characteristics) of a food product. The foods to be tested are often given a symbol so that the tasters are not influenced in any way. There are guidelines, British Standard BS5929, which the industry has to follow when carrying out sensory testing.

Ranking tests ➡

This is used by tasters to put food in order of preference, starting with the one they like best. You could ask the testers to place five different types of crisps in order. Alternatively, you could ask them to place crisps in rank order according to how salty they are.

Rating tests

These are used to show how much the tasters like or dislike a product. In these tests the food is given a score. You should always use an odd number so that the middle number can be used if tasters neither like nor dislike the product. Any odd number will do but five is a good scale as it is easy to use:

1 dislike a lot **2** dislike a little **3** neither like nor dislike **4** like a little **5** like a lot.

It is a good idea to use smiley faces instead of numbers if you are working with young children.

When you have collected your sensory analysis recording sheets you can add up the total scores. This will help you to see which was the preferred product.

Star profiles

Star profiles rate different attributes (characteristics) of the food. You will need to think of all the characteristics you want to test and then draw a star diagram with the same number of 'legs'. (Star diagrams can have any number of legs from three upwards.)

Write the attributes you are testing at the end of each leg. Divide the legs into five-point scales – use a ruler to measure accurately. The tasters are asked to give the product a mark out of five for each attribute. These are marked on the legs of the star. When the test is finished the marks are joined up. Using the information from several stars, it is possible to write a detailed profile for the product.

Comparative testing

There are several comparative tests which are used in the food industry, including **paired comparisons**, **triangle**, **A-not-A** and **threshold** testing. These are often used when a new product is being developed to mimic a product on the market.

Paired comparisons – Testers are given two products and asked to detect if there is a difference

Ranking Test	Name	
Taste the samples and put them in the order you like best.		
sample code	order	comments
◆		
○		
□		
★		

Fig. 1.42 *A ranking test*

Rating score	☹ 1	☹ 2	😐 3	🙂 4	😊 5
Sample ◆					
Sample ○					
Sample □					
Sample ★					

Fig. 1.43 *A rating test*

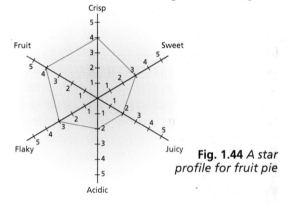

Fig. 1.44 *A star profile for fruit pie*

in them, usually concentrating on one characteristic such as sweetness.

Threshold testing – Reducing the amount of sugar used in a product would be one example of this. Testers will be asked when they can detect a change in the sweetness of a product. This allows the manufacturer to test how much sugar can be removed without changing the flavour.

A-not-A – This is sometimes called a **duo-trio** test. Testers are given one example to test, sample A. They are then given two other samples and they have to decide which is different to the first sample they tried, e.g. it is **not A**.

Triangle testing – Three samples are given to the tester, two of which are identical. The tester is asked to find the 'odd one out'. In school testing make sure you remember which is the 'odd one out'! This type of testing is often used by manufacturers when they are developing a recipe to copy a product made by a competitor.

Planning

Planning is a very important part of the design process. Careful planning will enable you to turn your ideas into reality (realisation). Planning your work thoroughly will help to prevent you from making mistakes and wasting both ingredients and time.

Before you can begin making your product you must ask yourself some questions.

Planning can be divided into three main areas: **product planning**, **resource planning** and **action planning**.

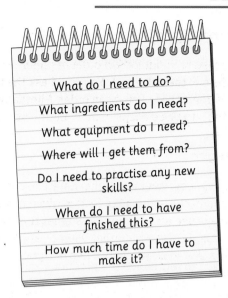

What do I need to do?

What ingredients do I need?

What equipment do I need?

Where will I get them from?

Do I need to practise any new skills?

When do I need to have finished this?

How much time do I have to make it?

Fig. 1.45 *You will need to ask yourself questions*

Product planning

Once you have formed your design proposals, think very carefully about how you are going to make your product. You must make a number of decisions (for example, how many portions it will make and how it will be finished). The information and sketches in your design proposals will help you to make these decisions. You may need to prepare **working drawings** of your product. These should be good enough to be used by someone else to produce your design. Remember that, in industry, the person who designs the product is not always the person who makes it.

Planning is important in your school work, but it is even more important in industry. In industry, products are not usually made entirely by one person. The separate components could be made in different parts of the country and assembled somewhere else. The planning you do needs to give as much information as possible, to guarantee that the product will look and taste the way it was planned.

Exploded drawings

Exploded drawings are useful when you want to show how something is assembled. They will help you to plan the making of your product. Exploded drawings are useful in food manufacturing to ensure that the product is assembled in the correct order.

Cross-sections

It is not always easy to understand how a product should look inside. Cross-sections are diagrams which show the product with a piece of it cut out. By 'cutting' the product we are able to see how it should look.

Plan (a birds' eye view)

It is often useful to be able to see the top of a product, especially if the food is to be finished in a particular way. Diagrams are simple ways of communicating this information to the person who will be responsible for finishing the product. Diagrams or photographs are often included in manufacturing specifications.

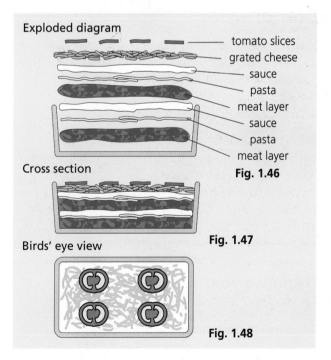

Exploded diagram

— tomato slices
— grated cheese
— sauce
— pasta
— meat layer
— sauce
— pasta
— meat layer

Cross section

Fig. 1.46

Fig. 1.47

Birds' eye view

Fig. 1.48

Portion control

It is important that food is equally divided into portions, both in the home and in industry. You must plan how your product will be divided into portions before you begin making it.

Resource planning

Drawings, sketches and photographs will all show how your finished product will look, but you will also need to make a detailed list of all the ingredients and equipment that you will need to make your product. You will be able to use your ingredients list to work out the cost of your finished product. You can use either price lists or a spreadsheet to work this out.

Ingredients lists

The ingredients list forms part of the **manufacturing or product specification**. The manufacturing specification will include:

- exact quantities of ingredients;
- cooking time;
- method of serving;
- temperature of cooking;
- type of flour, sugar, etc. to be used;
- method of shaping.

This will allow you to reproduce the product accurately again in future. This is very important in industry if a consistent product is to be manufactured.

Manufacturing Specification

Enriched bread-spiced buns

PORTION CONTROL: Divide the mixture equally into 6 by weight

INGREDIENTS	WEIGHT	INGREDIENTS	WEIGHT
Strong plain flour	200 g	Mixed peel	50 g
Caster sugar	5 g	Unsalted butter	50 g
Salt	2 g	Water at 39°C	75 ml

Fig. 1.49 *Points to include on a manufacturing specification*

You will also need to make a list of all the equipment that you will need to gather together before you can begin to make your product. Don't forget to include items such as pastry brushes, oil for greasing or flour dredgers.

Fig. 1.50 *Using a probe*

← **Have you forgotten anything?**

Check your list carefully. Is there anything you have forgotten? It is a good idea to get a friend to check your list for you.

Fig. 1.51 *A resources list*

Organise your resources

Look at your list of ingredients. Where will you get these from? Ask yourself the following questions:

- Can I order them from school? How much will I need to pay?
- Can I bring them from home? (Remember to ask in plenty of time, say, two or three days before the lesson.)

- Are some of the ingredients in the freezer? Will they need defrosting before I can use them? If so, when will I need to get them out of the freezer?
- Which fresh ingredients will I need to buy the day before the lesson? How much will they cost?

Tick the ingredients you can order from school or bring from home. Make a list of the items you will still have to find and write down where you will buy them from.

Action planning

To make sure that you make the best use of your time, energy and resources it is important to make a plan of action that you can follow.

Before starting to make your product you must plan what you are going to do. It is important to remember that some tasks need to be completed before others. For example, when making an apple pie you will need to make pastry for the pie and line the pie dish before you peel the apples. Some things take a long time to cook and these need to be started first. You must be sure that you can make the product you have planned within the time of the lesson.

Block diagrams ➡

Action planning requires you to be logical. You must work out what needs to be done and in what order. The simplest way to make a plan is in a block diagram. Write down all the tasks that need to be done, then put them in order. Draw a box around each task. You may be able to group related tasks together in one box. The boxes show the stages in the making process. Link these together with arrows. Fig. 1.52 shows a block diagram for making an apple crumble. Use the method listed in your recipe to work out all the stages you will need to complete.

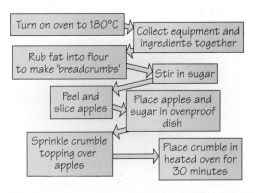

Fig. 1.52 *Block diagram for making an apple crumble*

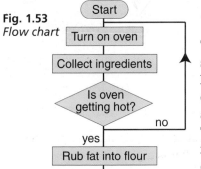

Fig. 1.53 *Flow chart*

⬅ Flow charts

The stages involved in making something can be shown as a flow chart like the one in Fig. 1.53. A number of different symbols are used to show the action involved in the making process. The British Standards Institution has recommended a list of symbols so that everyone involved can recognise them.

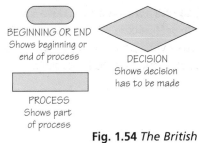

Fig. 1.54 *The British Standards Institution symbols used in flow charts*

Some projects will take several weeks to complete and you will need to plan ahead. You will need to estimate how long it will take to complete each part of the process. A work plan for the whole term may be needed. This can be set out as a block diagram or a flow chart, or you may prefer to use the method shown in Fig. 1.56.

Time	Order of work	Special points
9.00	Turn on oven, collect equipment and ingredients	Check oven is getting hot
9.10	Rub fat into flour until it resembles breadcrumbs	Shake bowl to see if any large pieces of fat are left
9.20	Stir in sugar, wash hands	
9.25	Peel, core and slice apples	Wrap waste in paper and place in bin
9.35	Put apples and sugar in oven proof dish	
9.40	Cover apples with crumble and place in oven	Use oven gloves
9.45	Wash up	

Fig. 1.55 *An example of a time plan*

If you are planning practical work for one lesson you may need to make a time plan. Remember that your product will need to be finished and your work area cleaned within the lesson time. Time plans usually divide the work into five- or ten-minute intervals. Allow time at the end for your product to cool and for you to wash items used for cooking, such as cake tins.

Work plan					
Week	Task	Equipment required	Work	Class	Home-work
1					
2					
3					
4					
5					
6					

Fig 1.56 *A work plan*

Making

After you have planned your product you will be ready to turn your plans into reality (realisation). This is the making stage. For many people this is the most enjoyable and exciting part of D & T.

Be prepared

In most cases making your product will not be too difficult. If you have thought carefully about what you are going to make, and planned and prepared properly, then the making should be straightforward. You will need to have organised all of your ingredients for the lesson and have a copy of the recipe and method to follow. If you do not understand any of the words in the recipe, such as 'whisk' or 'rub-in', make sure that you find out the meaning beforehand.

Fig. 1.57 *Clean your work surface before you begin*

◀ Hygiene

It is important that food is handled carefully. Food poisoning can be caused by not following good hygiene rules.

- jumper off;
- shirt sleeves rolled up;
- clean apron;
- hair tied back or wear a hair net like those worn in industry;
- hands washed;
- no nail varnish or jewellery;
- work surfaces should be cleaned with an anti-bacterial cleaner;
- use a clean dish cloth, tea towel and oven gloves.

Before you begin ➡

Before you start preparing food check that you are ready.

- Are all the ingredients available?
- Are they weighed accurately?
- Is all the equipment ready?
- Are the oven shelves correctly spaced?

- Is the oven turned on?
- Is the manufacturing specification available?
- Are the tins lined and greased?

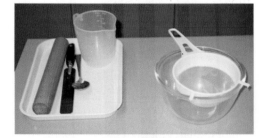
Fig. 1.58 *Collect your equipment*

If you are unsure of any techniques ask your teacher to demonstrate them before your practical session.

Aim for quality

Always aim to produce work of the highest quality. Remember that your product will be tested by other people – you may be taking it home to your family! Work carefully and accurately and keep checking that you have sufficient time to finish the work.

 Work safely

Safety is very important when working with tools, equipment and hot pans. It is at this stage that most accidents are likely to happen. Always try to be aware of the dangers and work as safely as possible.

- Keep the area around you clean and put things away or stack them at the side of the sink when you have finished with them.

- Never run in the food technology rooms.
- Carry knives with the blades facing the floor.
- Try not to carry hot things around the room.
- Pan handles should be turned to the side to avoid pans being knocked off.
- Always use oven gloves, not tea towels, to lift food out of the oven.
- Follow the safety rules of your food technology room.

Evaluating

Evaluating is a natural part of designing. It is very unusual for a person to design and make a product without considering how successful it is. Very few people are completely satisfied with their work. Most people, if they are being honest, will be able to suggest how they could improve their product. You will evaluate your work without realising it when you taste your food and add more seasoning or look at it and decide to add a garnish or decoration to improve the appearance.

Design activities do not always have to begin with identifying needs and opportunities. Evaluating an existing product can provide you with many opportunities for designing. You may choose to improve an existing product or you may decide to redesign it completely. Fig. 1.59 shows how evaluating can be the starting point for design work.

Fig. 1.59

Evaluate an existing artefact, system or environment → Identify needs and opportunities for designing → Generate new design proposals (improvements or redesign) for your own product → Plan and make your own product → Evaluate your own product

Ongoing evaluation

It is easy to think that evaluations only take place at the end of a project but this is not so. Ongoing or progressive evaluations occur throughout the designing and making process. It is very important to evaluate your work as it progresses. Keep notes and sketches or photographs. These can be used when you write your final evaluation. Fig. 1.60 gives you some idea of the types of questions you should ask yourself at each stage.

Fig. 1.60

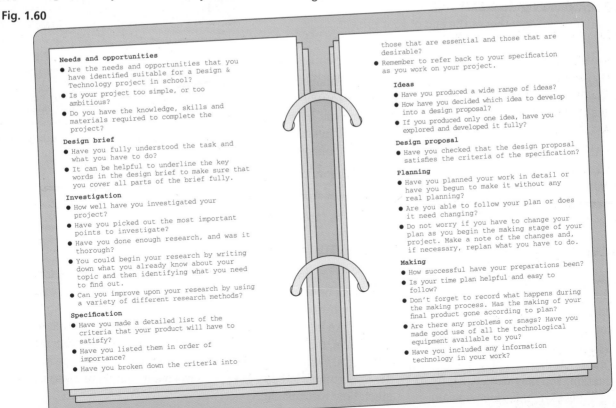

Needs and opportunities
● Are the needs and opportunities that you have identified suitable for a Design & Technology project in school?
● Is your project too simple, or too ambitious?
● Do you have the knowledge, skills and materials required to complete the project?

Design brief
● Have you fully understood the task and what you have to do?
● It can be helpful to underline the key words in the design brief to make sure that you cover all parts of the brief fully.

Investigation
● How well have you investigated your project?
● Have you picked out the most important points to investigate?
● Have you done enough research, and was it thorough?
● You could begin your research by writing down what you already know about your topic and then identifying what you need to find out.
● Can you improve upon your research by using a variety of different research methods?

Specification
● Have you made a detailed list of the criteria that your product will have to satisfy?
● Have you listed them in order of importance?
● Have you broken down the criteria into those that are essential and those that are desirable?
● Remember to refer back to your specification as you work on your project.

Ideas
● Have you produced a wide range of ideas?
● How have you decided which idea to develop into a design proposal?
● If you produced only one idea, have you explored and developed it fully?

Design proposal
● Have you checked that the design proposal satisfies the criteria of the specification?

Planning
● Have you planned your work in detail or have you begun to make it without any real planning?
● Are you able to follow your plan or does it need changing?
● Do not worry if you have to change your plan as you begin the making stage of your project. Make a note of the changes and, if necessary, replan what you have to do.

Making
● How successful have your preparations been?
● Is your time plan helpful and easy to follow?
● Don't forget to record what happens during the making process. Has the making of your final product gone according to plan?
● Are there any problems or snags? Have you made good use of all the technological equipment available to you?
● Have you included any information technology in your work?

Testing

You will need to test the flavour, texture and appearance of your product as it develops. This will involve some form of sensory analysis (see page 19). Using the results of your sensory analysis you will be able to change the proportions or types of ingredients until you achieve a successful final product.

If your product has been designed to be a frozen or cook-chill product, you will need to keep a sample to freeze or chill and reheat. Not all foods are suitable for these methods of processing. After freezing, for example, some flavours become more noticeable. Products like cornflour sauces do not always reheat successfully. It is vital that these tests are carried out carefully.

 If you are not sure that the food is safe, do not eat the reheated sample but use your other senses to help you test it.

When you have developed your final solution you will need to conduct sensory testing as well as tests which determine how long a shelf life your product has. If you have been asked to design packaging, you will need to evaluate whether the packaging will keep the food in the best possible condition during its shelf life.

Final evaluation

The records of ongoing evaluations which you keep can be incorporated into your final evaluation. The final evaluation is put together at the end of your project.

Evaluating your finished product

You need to have something to judge your product against if your evaluation is to be useful. Think back to your specification. Do you remember how you thought carefully about the criteria that the finished product must satisfy? You can now evaluate your finished product against those criteria. Does it fulfil all the criteria in the specification, or just some of them? Fig. 1.61 shows a checklist which can be used to help you with your evaluation.

Admit your mistakes

Try not to give vague answers like 'yes' or 'it did not taste nice'. Wherever possible, give reasons for your answer. For example, 'My pastry was difficult to roll out because I had the wrong proportions of fat and flour. Next time I will check that my ingredients are weighed accurately.' It is important to be honest if you are to learn how to avoid making the same mistakes in the future. You will be credited with being able to evaluate your work fairly if you are honest.

I have finished my new project and it seems to meet all the criteria of my specification. I worked well on my own and used my time wisely. It was useful making a time plan to follow for the practical lessons, this helped me to be more organised than I have been in the past.

I tested my finished dish at home by asking my family to fill in a rating test when they had eaten it. It scored 17 out of a possible 20. This was very good.

If I were to make this product again I would try to make sure that I cut all the vegetables evenly so that they cooked at the same time.

Fig. 1.61

Checklist
1. What were my original aims?
2. How does my finished product meet these aims?
3. How successful is the product? Does it work?
4. Am I happy with the results?
5. What do other people think about my design work?
6. Can I improve the product in any way?

Other people's evaluation

It can be difficult to be **objective** (fair) about something you have made yourself so it is a good idea to ask other people to test your product for you. Record their views and use the information in the final evaluation. You may need to set up a taste panel to do this (see page 19).

Improving your finished product

Could you improve your finished product in any way? You are either very lucky or very talented if the answer is no. Nearly every piece of work can be improved. The improvement may be something very simple, like improving the presentation by adding a garnish or decoration, or it may be more complicated, such as altering the nutritional value of the product or its shelf life. You may be given the opportunity to carry out your improvements, depending on how much time is available.

Presenting your final evaluation

For your first evaluations you are likely to be given questions to answer about your finished product, the project and how you completed it. As you become more experienced, the evaluation will become a larger part of your work. Although the evaluation will be a written piece of work, you should use sketches, diagrams or photographs to illustrate it. (If you have a digital camera, photographs will be more readily available.)

Don't forget to include any changes or improvements that could be made. You should also think about how you worked. If you were asked to do this piece of work again, what would you do differently?

Fig 1.62 *Using a computer will help with your final evaluation*

Evaluating in industry

Evaluation is a very important task in industry. Companies continually evaluate how they are making products in order to produce goods as efficiently, safely and competitively as possible. Consumers are often asked to evaluate products as part of market research so that the company can take the consumers' views into consideration. Most food products which appear on the market are the result of the work of industrial designers in evaluating and changing existing products. The need for changes may be due to one or more of the following reasons:

- Falling sales – manufacturers need to maintain the amount of sales of a product if they are to continue making a profit. All products have a life cycle. When sales begin to fall, a re-launch will help to lift the sales figures.

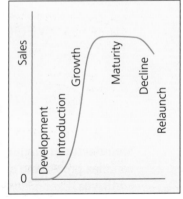

Fig. 1.64 *The life cycle of a new product*

- Competition from rival products may force changes to be made. Manufacturers need to stay ahead of their competitors if they are to keep their share of the market.

Fig. 1.65 *Rival products*

- Fashion in foods – recent trends have included Thai, Japanese (Pacific Rim) cooking. Caribbean cooking is also becoming popular. This can be a result of people visiting these countries on holiday, or of magazines, supermarkets and TV food programmes promoting these styles of cooking.

Fig. 1.66 *Thai food*

Fig. 1.63 *Low-fat foods*

- Changes in customer demands – e.g. the demand for low-fat or low-sugar products created the opportunity for many existing products to be manufactured in low-fat or low-sugar varieties.

- New technology can alter methods of production in industry or in the home. For example, microwave ovens created an opportunity for many new products.
- New ingredients appear, like the cellulose which is added to create 'high fibre 'drinks.

The design process is never completed. Each time a product is evaluated it may lead to a change being suggested. Sometimes products are removed from the market entirely and new products are launched. Industry relies on new designs to provide jobs and to earn money for the UK through exports. Consumers rely on new products to meet their changing needs.

2 INGREDIENTS

All our foods are produced from ingredients, or **components** as they are called in the food industry. All components can be divided into three main groups – **primary**, **secondary** and **tertiary**. Different methods of processing allow the development from one group on to the next group of foods.

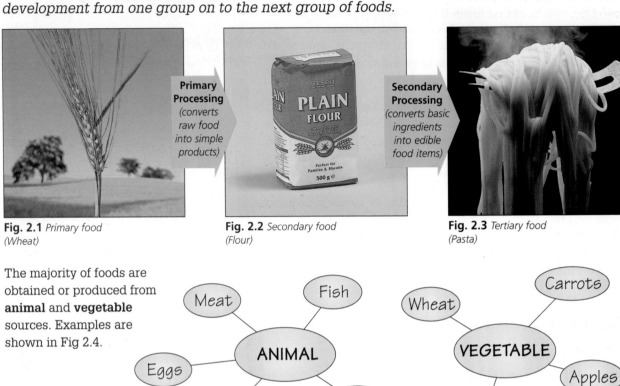

Primary Processing (converts raw food into simple products)

Secondary Processing (converts basic ingredients into edible food items)

Fig. 2.1 *Primary food (Wheat)*

Fig. 2.2 *Secondary food (Flour)*

Fig. 2.3 *Tertiary food (Pasta)*

The majority of foods are obtained or produced from **animal** and **vegetable** sources. Examples are shown in Fig 2.4.

ANIMAL — Meat, Fish, Eggs, Cheese, Milk

VEGETABLE — Wheat, Carrots, Apples, Mushrooms

Fig. 2.4

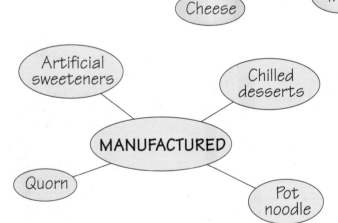

MANUFACTURED — Artificial sweeteners, Chilled desserts, Quorn, Pot noodle

Fig. 2.5

Manufactured products are made by complex processing and often use food **additives**. Examples are shown in Fig. 2.5.

When fresh ingredients are being prepared, it is obvious what is being eaten. However, when a manufactured product is bought (such as a cold dessert or meat pie), it may not be so easy to see what ingredients or components have been used to produce the product.

A variety of foods may cause **allergic reactions** in some people, and in some cases these reactions can be very severe. For example, some people have a very bad reaction to nuts. Labelling on products enables consumers to identify any ingredients to which they may be allergic.

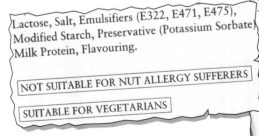

Lactose, Salt, Emulsifiers (E322, E471, E475), Modified Starch, Preservative (Potassium Sorbate) Milk Protein, Flavouring.

NOT SUITABLE FOR NUT ALLERGY SUFFERERS

SUITABLE FOR VEGETARIANS

| Pantothenic acid | 3.3mg | 55 | 1.8mg | 30 |
| Iron | 7.8mg | 55 | 3.6mg | 25 |

* Recommended Daily Allowance (RDA) according to the EC Nutrition Labelling Directive 90/496/EEC.
** Per Serving values include nutrients contributed by milk.
A 45g serving of Nestlé Shreddies provides 25% of the Recommended Daily Allowance (RDA) of 8 vitamins and iron. This pack contains approximately 11 servings each of 45 grams.

INGREDIENTS
Whole Grain Wheat, Sugar, Malt Extract, Salt, Antioxidant: Tocopherols. Vitamins and Minerals: Niacin, Pantothenic Acid, Vitamin B6, Thiamin (B1), Riboflavin (B2), Vitamin D, Folic Acid (Folacin), Vitamin B12 and Iron.
Manufactured in a facility that processes nuts

Fig. 2.6 *Labels warn if nuts are used in a product*

Choosing ingredients

When choosing ingredients, careful thought has to be given to the type of product that is being produced. For example:

■ Who is it for?
■ How will it be processed?

The main properties of the ingredients used must be considered. These properties can be:

■ **functional** – e.g. to thicken, add shine or bind ingredients together;
■ **sensory** – e.g. to add flavour, aroma, texture or to improve the appearance;
■ **nutritional** – e.g. using low-fat yogurt and fromage frais in place of full-fat varieties.

Functional properties

When a product is developed each ingredient used carries out a function, as shown in Fig. 2.7.

More information about working with ingredients can be found in Chapter 3.

Fig. 2.7 *The function of ingredients*

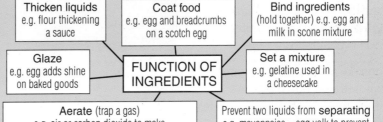

Thicken liquids
e.g. flour thickening a sauce

Coat food
e.g. egg and breadcrumbs on a scotch egg

Bind ingredients
(hold together) e.g. egg and milk in scone mixture

Glaze
e.g. egg adds shine on baked goods

FUNCTION OF INGREDIENTS

Set a mixture
e.g. gelatine used in a cheesecake

Aerate (trap a gas)
e.g. air or carbon dioxide to make the mixture light as in flaky pastry, cakes, bread

Prevent two liquids from **separating**
e.g. mayonnaise – egg yolk to prevent vinegar and oil separating

Sensory properties

Our senses play a very important part in enjoying food. Food should be prepared and served attractively so that its **appearance** stimulates people to want to eat it. A good variety of **colours** is needed to achieve this.

Textures also add interest. Products which have only one texture can lack a satisfying 'mouth feel'. A product with several texture experiences, such as a crunchy biscuit base, smooth, soft topping and chewy decoration can be more satisfying.

Fig. 2.9 *Stewed apples and rice pudding provide similar texture experiences*

The **aroma** of a product, such as bread, being prepared or cooked stimulates the appetite. It also creates an expectation of the flavour of the food. This is why supermarkets sometimes pipe the smell of freshly baked bread to the entrance of the store so that customers are subconsciously encouraged to purchase bread.

Many ingredients can be used to add **flavour** to products. Some are natural flavours, such as onion, garlic, bacon, herbs and spices, but a wide variety of flavours can also be created using food chemicals.

Fig. 2.8 *The attractive appearance of this lemon cheesecake makes people want to eat it*

Nutritional properties

Much advice has been given to the British population to encourage better eating habits to improve our general health. Fig. 2.10 gives some advice about how to get the right balance when choosing foods.

Choose foods from all four groups and aim to match this balance every day

Cereals & starchy vegetables

Fruit & vegetables

Meat, fish & alternatives

Milk & milk products

Fig. 2.10

Ingredients: animal

Eggs

Chickens are the most popular source of eggs in Britain. The largest number of eggs is obtained from **battery** or **deep litter** farming, with a smaller number from **free range** chickens. The large-scale farming of chickens has enabled eggs to be one of the cheapest **high biological value** protein foods available.

Eggs are graded according to standards set down by the European Union (EU). This grades eggs in sizes ranging from size 1 (weighing 70 g or over) to size 7 (with a weight of under 45 g). An average egg is size 4, which has a weight of 55–60 g.

Eggs have many uses in food preparation which add valuable characteristics to the products. These are highlighted in Fig. 2.13.

Fig. 2.11 *Free range chickens*

Fig. 2.12 *Battery hens*

Sensory properties

Garnish – eggs can be cooked and used as a garnish to products (e.g. sliced hard boiled egg, shredded omelette).
Glazing – beaten whole egg or yolk can be used to create a shiny glaze on pastry. Egg white and sugar creates a crystallised glaze on sweet pastry products.

Functional properties

Binding – beaten eggs bind ingredients together so they hold their shape when cooked.
Coating – beaten eggs are used to coat products and enable dry ingredients to be attached (e.g. breadcrumbs).
Emulsifier – eggs contain lecithin which prevents oil and water mixtures separating (e.g. salad dressing)
Foaming – beaten eggs form a structure which enables a mixture to hold air (e.g. meringues).
Thickening – beaten egg can be used to thicken products (e.g. egg custard or lemon meringue pie).

Nutritional properties

Eggs are a valuable source of high biological value protein, vitamin B group, calcium and phosphorus.

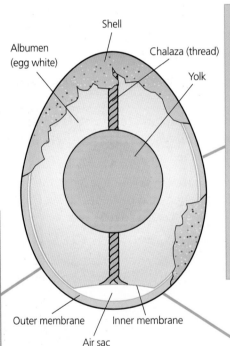

Shell
Albumen (egg white)
Chalaza (thread)
Yolk
Outer membrane
Inner membrane
Air sac

Fig. 2.13 *Cross-section of an egg*

Storage of eggs

Eggs should be kept in a cold place like a refrigerator or pantry. When eggs are mixed into a food product they will freeze successfully. Do not freeze eggs in the shell as they will crack.

Fig. 2.14 *Egg products*

List the functions of eggs used to produce the products in Fig. 2.14.

 Always wash hands after handling eggs.

Fish

Fish is a highly nutritious food which can be used in a variety of ways. For example, it can be poached, battered or included in pies, bakes and curries. Fish is quick to cook, so care has to be taken not to overcook it, as it will become dry and develop a tough texture. Particular care needs to be taken, however, to fully cook all shellfish for the correct amount of time so they are safe to eat. Further information on cooking fish can be found in Chapter 3.

Fig. 2.15 *Fish display*

Fish are obtained from salt water (sea) or fresh water (rivers and lakes). They can be grouped according to shape or the amount of fat they contain. The more common groupings are:

White fish – has white flesh (e.g. cod, haddock, plaice, skate, sole and halibut).

Oily fish – has darker flesh (e.g. herring, sardines, mackerel, salmon, trout, squid and octopus).

Shellfish – has a shell (e.g. crab, lobster, prawns, mussels and oysters)

Cuts of fish

Fish can be bought whole or cut as shown in Fig. 2.16.

Sensory properties

Fish has a delicate flavour.

Fish is easy to chew.

Some processing techniques produce different flavours (e.g. canned salmon and smoked haddock).

Functional properties

Fish is easy to digest.

Fish can be served in a variety of ways (e.g. steak, fillet or flaked and mixed in with other ingredients).

One type of fish can be successfully replaced by a similar type of fish (e.g. cod replaced by haddock).

A fish from another grouping can also replace a named fish but will produce different results e.g. colour or flavour.

Fish can be processed in many ways (e.g. canning, freezing, pickling).

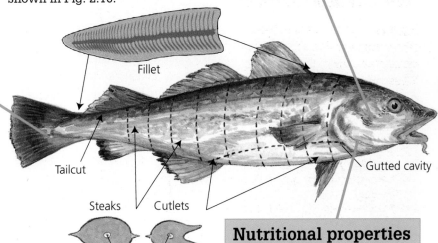

Fillet

Tailcut

Steaks Cutlets

Bone

Gutted cavity

Storage of fish

Wet fish should be loosely wrapped in greaseproof paper and polythene and placed on the bottom shelf of the refrigerator.

Canned fish will store for long periods of time but must be used by the date given on the can.

Storage of frozen fish depends on how cold the freezer is. An upright or chest freezer will store items more safely than the freezer compartment of a refrigerator. In this case frozen fish must be used within:

- white fish – 3 months;
- oily fish – 2 months;
- shellfish – 1 month.

Nutritional properties

Fish is usually the main protein food of a meal.

Fish contains protein of a high biological value.

Oily fish contains high quantities of vitamin D and essential fatty acids which are important to our health.

Fish with edible bones (e.g. sardines and canned tuna), contain high quantities of calcium. Cockles and mussels contain high quantities of iron.

 Ensure fish is thoroughly cooked before eating.

Meat

In Britain, meat is classified as any part of **cattle**, **sheep**, or **pigs** but in other countries traditional meats might be the flesh of horses, asses or goats. The meat of an animal can be part of the carcass (the body) or internal organs (**offal**), such as the kidneys or liver.

Fig. 2.17 *Lamb, chicken and beef are some of the meats eaten most often in this country*

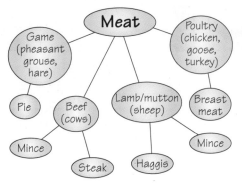

Fig. 2.18

Other sources of meat include **poultry** (e.g. chicken, goose and turkey) which is bred by farmers, and wild **game** (e.g. pheasant, grouse and hare) which is hunted.

Many products are made from different types of meat. There are detailed regulations (laws) in force to ensure that only high quality products are produced. If a manufacturer does not follow these regulations accurately he would be prosecuted and fined. For example, beefburgers must contain at least 80% beef with at least 65% lean meat.

Functional properties

- Thin cuts of meat, e.g. chops or steak, can be grilled or fried.
- Thicker cuts of meat, e.g. shoulder (lamb) or brisket (beef), require longer, slower cooking to make them tender to eat.
- Different cuts of meat can be used to replace a meat named in a recipe as long as they require the same type of cooking.
- Meats can be used to produce a variety of other products, e.g. sausages and pies.
- Frozen cuts of meats can be stored successfully for long periods of time.
- Meat will become very tender when cooked in liquid on a low heat for a long period of time.

Sensory properties

- Dry methods of cooking, e.g. grilling or frying, give extra flavour to meats.
- Meat has a denser structure than fish and so it requires more chewing.
- Meat has a satisfying taste and aroma when cooked.

Nutritional properties

- Meat contains valuable sources of high quality protein.
- Meat is a good source of vitamin B and iron.
- The fat content of meat can be reduced by cutting off visible fat.

Storage of meat

All **raw meats** should be covered and placed in a container on the bottom shelf of a refrigerator (to prevent meat juices dripping onto other foods) or in a freezer.

Cooked meats that need to be stored should be cooled, covered, placed in the refrigerator and used as soon as possible to prevent the growth of bacteria.

Frozen meats and **meat products** should be thawed completely before being cooked unless otherwise instructed on the packaging. The best way to thaw frozen meat and poultry is to place it in a container in the fridge where it will thaw well with the temperature never rising above the safe limit of 5°C.

 Wash hands and equipment after handling raw meats. Separate equipment should always be used for cooked and uncooked meats. This prevents bacteria from passing from uncooked meats onto cooked meats, which could cause food poisoning.

Fig. 2.19 *Raw meat should be covered and stored on the bottom shelf of a refrigerator*

Milk and milk products

Milk is a liquid food which is high in easily digested nutrients. Milk and the foods made from it are known as **dairy products**.

Milk can be processed in many ways. The processes used create products which may have advantages over fresh milk. For example, the product may have a longer shelf life, be able to be stored at room temperature, or be able to be stored for use in emergencies.

There may also be disadvantages to the processes used. For example, the flavour may be altered or high quantities of sugar may be added.

The choice of milk used depends on personal preference. A different type of milk can replace milk in a product, e.g. semi-skimmed milk can be used in place of whole milk.

Milk is used to produce many other products. See Fig. 2.21.

Milk can be used in many different ways.

Fig. 2.20 *Types of milk*

Milk — Butter, Ice-cream, Yoghurts, Cheese spread, Processed cheese slices, Cheddar cheese, Quark, Cottage cheese, Fromage frais, Soured cream, Clotted cream, Double cream, Whipping cream, Single cream

Fig. 2.21

Fig. 2.22 *Milk products*

Functional properties

■ Enriches mixtures such as custards, sauces and batters, e.g. pancakes.
■ Binds mixtures, e.g. scones and cakes.
■ Adds nutrients to products.

Sensory properties

■ Creates a smooth and creamy texture, e.g. in hot milky drinks, puddings and as cream added to soups.
■ Creates an attractive appearance, e.g. glazes on pastry or bread products and cream piped onto dessert.
■ Provides contrasting texture, e.g. yogurt served with fruit.
■ Provides contrasting colours, e.g. melted cheese on potato.

Nutritional properties

■ Milk contains high quality protein.
■ Useful quantities of the vitamin B group, vitamin D and calcium are present in milk.
■ Full-cream milk is high in fat.

Storage of milk and milk products

All milk products should be stored in a chilled environment unless otherwise stated on the packaging. Storage times depend on the method used to process the milk. Once opened or reconstituted, sterilised and dried milk should be treated just like fresh milk.

 All 'use by' dates should be carefully noted so that products are used in date order.

Ingredients: vegetable

Cereals

Cereals are the **seeds** of **cultivated grasses**. They include **wheat**, **barley**, **rye**, **oats**, **maize** or **corn** and **rice**.

Cereals are important foods in every country and are classified as a staple food (that is, they are a basic part of the nation's diet).

Wheat is the most common cereal used in Britain but many other cereals are also extremely popular for a variety of different uses. In their raw state cereals are primary foods. Breakfast cereals (e.g. Weetabix, Rice Krispies and Shredded Wheat) are processed foods because they have gone through a variety of processes during production.

A variety of ingredients within this group can be used to replace another similar ingredient. For example, **wholemeal flour** can be used to replace part or all of the required quantity of white flour in a product. This change alters the flavour and consistency of the mixture. In this case, extra liquid will be required to achieve the correct consistency as the bran in the wholemeal flour also absorbs some liquid.

Cereal	Ingredient	Use
Wheat	Flour – plain and self-raising	Biscuits, cakes, shortcrust and choux pastries, and thickening mixtures
	– Strong	Breads, flaky pastries and pasta
	– Wholemeal/ wheatmeal	Pastries, breads and pasta
Barley	Malt flour	Malt breads
	Pearl barley	Thickens soups and stews
Rye	Flour	Breads and crispbreads
Oats	Rolled oats	Muesli, porridge, cakes and biscuits
	Ground oatmeal	Oatcakes, digestive biscuits and haggis
Maize or corn	Corn-on-the-cob/ sweetcorn	Served with savoury products Cornflakes
	Flour	Custard powder, cornflour
Rice	Long-grain rice Short-grain rice/flakes Ground rice Rice paper	Curries and risottos Milk puddings Cakes, puddings, soups and biscuits Lining tins when baking biscuits or for edible decorations (using food colouring pens)

Storage of cereals

Dried cereals and cereal products need to be stored in air-tight containers to prevent moisture from creating ideal conditions for bacteria and moulds to grow. Other products made from cereals need to be stored according to type, e.g. bread or cakes can be frozen if they need to be stored for long periods.

Functional properties

■ Gives structure to a mixture, e.g. strong flour contains high quantities of gluten which provides the structure of bread. Any strong flour can be used but as the bran in brown flour absorbs liquid, more liquid is required in brown or wholemeal breads to ensure the correct texture is achieved.

■ It is the main ingredient of a mixture, e.g. scones. Flour makes up the largest proportion of ingredients contained in the mixture, therefore the type of flour chosen will affect the end result.

Sensory properties

■ Thickens liquids, e.g. sauces, soups, stews, puddings.
■ Adds contrasting colour, e.g. rice with curry, sweetcorn.
■ Adds texture, e.g. creates chewy textures in stews, and flaky and crisp textures in pastries.
■ Adds flavour, e.g. malt flour used in malt loaf.

1 Describe the differences in the breads shown in Fig. 2.23. Which bread contains the most nutrition? Why?

2 Research a variety of products which include cereals in their ingredients lists.

3 Produce a table to record the product, the cereal used and the function that the cereal performs.

Fig. 2.23

Nutritional properties

Cereals vary in nutritional value but in general they:

■ contain an excellent source of carbohydrate in the form of starch;
■ are good sources of protein and the vitamin B group;
■ provide valuable sources of non-starch polysaccharide (dietary fibre);
■ provide iron and some B vitamins which are added to bread by law.

Nuts and pulses

Nuts are seeds or fruits which have a hard edible kernel within a hard shell, for example, coconut, Brazil nuts, walnuts, almonds, cashews and chestnuts.

Pulses are the seeds of plants. They can be grouped as beans, seeds and peas. Examples include red kidney beans, haricot beans, butter beans, soya beans, lentils and whole or split peas.

Fig. 2.24 *Nuts and pulses*

Functional properties

- They **thicken** mixtures. For example, lentils or split peas can be added to stews or ground nuts to liquids.
- They add **bulk** to products, e.g. chopped nuts added to stuffings.
- Soya beans are used to **manufacture** textured vegetable protein and tofu which are both protein-rich meat substitutes (see page 38).
- Pulses can be used as a vegetable **accompaniment** to a meal, e.g. baked beans which are manufactured from haricot beans.
- They add **nutrients** to products.

The pulses and nuts used in a product can be altered according to preference. Obviously the flavour of the end product will vary according to the choices made.

Nuts and pulses add valuable nutrition, textures and flavours to products. They also form many of the basic foods eaten in vegetarian diets.

Sensory properties

- They add **texture** to products, e.g. nuts added to salads.
- They add **decoration** to products, e.g. nuts on an iced cake or nuts as a **garnish** on vegetables.
- They add **flavour** to products, e.g. red kidney beans in stew.
- Pulses add **interest** to products by providing a good variety of **colours** and **sizes**.

Nutritional properties

- Pulses and nuts provide good sources of **low biological value protein**.
- Pulses and nuts provide excellent sources of **non-starch polysaccharides** (dietary fibre) and calcium.
- Pulses are a fairly good source of **iron** and **vitamin B**, while nuts contain higher quantities of **vitamin B**.
- Nuts are rich in fat so are a concentrated form of **energy**.

Fig. 2.25 *Nuts are often used to decorate food items*

Storage of nuts and pulses

Nuts and pulses have a good shelf life. If stored in airtight containers, out of direct sunlight, they should last up to six months.

Pulses are readily available in dried, canned and made-up products.

Nuts are obtainable as whole pieces or blanched, chopped and ground in a variety of sized packets. Nuts are also used to produce spreads, such as peanut butter, and can be incorporated with other flavours, e.g. hazelnuts are mixed with chocolate in Nutella.

⚠ Ensure that all products containing nuts are clearly labelled as nuts can cause strong allergic reactions in some people. Dried red kidney beans must be soaked overnight and boiled for at least 15 minutes to destroy natural toxins (poisons) which will cause food poisoning if the beans are not fully cooked. It may be safer and quicker to use canned red kidney beans.

Fruits and vegetables

Fruits and vegetables are an important part of our diet as they add interesting flavours, colours and textures to our food. They also provide our main source of vitamin C.

Fig. 2.26 *A selection of fresh fruits and vegetables*

Due to excellent modern packaging and transportation methods, many varieties of fresh fruits and vegetables are now available all year round.

Processed fruits and vegetables are also available, such as frozen, canned and dried varieties. These can be successfully substituted if the fresh variety is unavailable. One disadvantage of using processed fruit and vegetables is that large quantities of salt and sugar may be added during the manufacturing processes. This can make them less healthy than the fresh varieties. Some canned fruits are available in natural juices, these contain less sugar than those canned in syrup.

Functional properties

- They are **easy to eat** as a snack.
- They can be **successfully processed** for a longer life, e.g. frozen, canned or dried.
- They can **thicken** mixtures through cooking or liquidising.
- Once opened, low-sugar products must be **stored in the fridge**.

Fig. 2.27 *Meringue with a fruit filling*

Sensory properties

- They add **colour**, **texture** and **flavour** to meals.
- They create a **light** and **refreshing** finish to a meal.
- They add **contrast to a meal**, e.g. apple sauce with roast pork.
- They add **decoration** or **garnish** to meals.
- High temperatures used in the canning process **create softer fruits** and vegetables.

Nutritional properties

- They provide the majority of **vitamin C** in our diet.
- Apricots, carrots and dark green vegetables provide **vitamin A**, **vitamin B** and small amounts of **iron** and **calcium**.
- Fruit and vegetables contain no **vitamin D**.
- They provide excellent quantities of **non-starch polysaccharides** (dietary fibre).
- Fruit and vegetables provide low quantities of **protein.**
- Vitamin C is **destroyed** during the drying process because of the extreme temperatures used.

Fig. 2.29 *Salad helps to make this a balanced meal*

Storage of fruits and vegetables

Both fruits and vegetables are perishable and need to be eaten as soon as possible after purchase. Most can be stored in the refrigerator to prevent ripening or in a dark cupboard to prevent sprouting.

Berried fruits (e.g. strawberries) quickly grow moulds so they need to be used on the day of purchase.

Bananas need to be stored separately as when they ripen they release a gas which causes other fruit to spoil.

Fig. 2.28 *Soft fruits should be eaten on the day when they were bought*

1. Name the fruits and vegetables in Figs 2.26.
2. Suggest three ways that fruits and vegetables could be effectively included in an average person's diet.
3. Research the variety of fruits and vegetables available in your local supermarket and compare the prices of fresh and processed varieties.

Sugar

Sugar is a very versatile food which fulfils many functions in food production. However, it contains virtually no nutritional value other than carbohydrate so sugar is said to contain 'empty calories'.

A lot of research has taken place to produce sweeteners with less energy value than sugar. The aim of this has been to enable people to enjoy sweet foods without the disadvantage of putting on weight or suffering from tooth decay. Although this research has been fairly successful, the results have not yet achieved the same effect or flavour as sugar.

Food technologists continue to develop artificial sweeteners which aim to produce successful results with no unpleasant aftertastes (see page 39). The most recent product on the market is 'Half-Spoon' which combines natural sugars and artificial sweeteners. It has yet to be seen how successful this product will prove.

Fig. 2.30 *Different types of sugar are used in different ways*

Functional properties

- Sugar is used in the **aeration** of creamed cakes because the fine crystals of caster sugar enable more air to be included in the mixture.
- Sugar aids **moisture retention** in cakes. This helps to make baked products soft.
- Sugar is the **main ingredient** in sweets and icings.
- Sugar is used as a preservative as large quantities of sugar create unsuitable conditions for bacteria, yeasts and moulds to grow.
- Sugar **stabilises** whisked mixtures (e.g. meringues) because it strengthens the foam.

Sensory properties

- Sugar is used for **caramelising**. During heating sugar turns from white to black, passing through all the different shades of brown in between. This adds to the colour of cakes and syrups.
- Sugar is used for **coating** other foods. Sugar syrups can be used as a glaze on pastries. Sugar can also be used to coat the surface of cut fruit. This prevents the oxygen in the air from turning white fruits brown (e.g. apples and bananas).
- Sugar adds **sweetness** to a mixture. Fresh and dried fruits and juices, honey, grated carrot or parsnip can all be used to sweeten food products naturally.
- Artificial sweeteners are used in the manufacture of **'low-sugar'**, **'low-calorie'**, **'diet'** and **diabetic products**.

Nutritional properties

- Sugar only provides carbohydrate.
- There is no nutritional difference between white and brown sugar.
- Molasses (treacle) does contain traces of vitamin B, iron and other minerals not found in brown sugar.
- Dried fruits and some vegetables, e.g. raisins, apricots, dates and carrots, can be used to sweeten products naturally. The nutrients they contain are also added to the food product being made.

Fig. 2.31

Storage of sugar

Sugar needs to be stored in airtight containers so that moisture and flavours do not taint (spoil) it.

Different-flavoured sugars can be made, e.g. by storing a vanilla pod in the sugar container. These flavoured sugars can be used when making cakes, biscuits and puddings.

Some low-sugar food products are now available, e.g. jams, cakes and biscuits. Once these jams are opened they need to be stored in the refrigerator to prevent the growth of bacteria and moulds.

Ingredients: manufactured

Manufactured ingredients have been processed to make them into products (e.g. frozen lasagne) or components (e.g. canned sauces, new protein foods and additives). Modern developments in machinery and food technology have enabled many processes to be carried out which were previously not possible. This progress (**technology push**), together with consumer demands (**consumer pull**), has brought about many new developments in the food industry.

At the same time many health issues have become important to consumers. As a result, increasing numbers of people are trying to eat healthier diets; by reducing fat, salt or sugar, increasing fibre or possibly even turning to a vegetarian diet. Many guidelines have been produced to help food manufacturers, catering establishments and consumers to find a healthier way of eating.

Fig. 2.32
New products have been developed to appeal to vegetarians

Novel (new) protein foods

As the majority of foods within the vegetable groups contain a different form of protein to animal foods, research has been carried out to improve the quality of protein in meat-free diets. As a result, some new foods have been produced (for example, Quorn). Developments have also been made to existing foods such as tofu to increase the quantities of protein they contain. Many people use these foods as meat substitutes because they feel they provide a healthier diet.

Fig. 2.33 *Novel protein foods*

(Diagram: Quorn Tofu Tivall — Nuggets, 'Burgers', 'Sausages', Fillets, Pies, Patés, Mince)

Functional properties

- Novel protein foods **replace meat** in meat-free products.
- Ready-prepared products (e.g. fillets and burgers) enable meals to be **prepared quickly**.
- Novel protein foods are available in **dried**, **chilled** and **frozen** forms.
- Some novel protein foods (e.g. textured vegetable protein or TVP) can be used to **add bulk** to a product at a lower price than using all meat.
- A **shorter cooking time** is required, compared to meat.

Sensory properties

- Novel protein foods add interesting textures in meat-free products.
- They need to absorb flavours from other foods to enable the best results to be achieved.
- They add contrasting colour to food products.

Nutritional properties

- Novel protein foods increase the protein value in meat-free products.
- They are nutritionally similar to meat.
- They increase the food value in ready-prepared products, e.g. Pot Noodle.

Storage of novel protein foods

Once opened, dried forms of novel protein food require storage in airtight containers. This is to prevent moisture from reconstituting the product and providing ideal conditions for bacteria to multiply.

Chilled and frozen varieties must be stored at the correct temperatures and must be completely cooked before serving.

All 'use by' dates must be followed accurately.

Additives

Consumers have high expectations about how they want their food to look, taste and keep.

Food additives help manufacturers to produce what the consumer wants. For example, the processes involved in preserving make glacé cherries turn dark purple, so a food colour is used to give the red shade that is expected.

Fig. 2.34 Glacé cherries before and after colouring

Fig. 2.35 Additives are used in many foods

Additives are **food chemicals** that are used to fulfil a variety of functions in food products. They can be obtained from natural sources or made synthetically, but both groups are classified as food chemicals because they have undergone processing to produce them.

Sensory properties

- To prevent the softening of food during cooking – **firming agent E227–578**.
- To thicken mixtures – **thickeners E400–466**.
- To produce a shiny appearance and protective surface – **glazing agents 901–904**.
- To increase the taste or smell of food – **flavour enhancer 620–637**.
- To add or replace colour lost during processing – **colours E100–180**.

Functional properties

- To increase the shelf life of a product by preventing the growth of bacteria, moulds and yeasts – **preservatives E200–290**.
- To prevent excessive frothing of mixtures – **anti-foaming agent 900**.
- To keep dry ingredients free flowing, e.g. dried cake mixture – **anti-caking agent E170–900**.
- To prevent the separation of liquids, e.g. salad dressing – **E322–495**.
- To sweeten a product, e.g. saccharin sweeteners – **E420–421**.

Nutritional properties

- To improve the **iron** and **vitamin** content in breakfast cereals.
- To improve the **vitamin C** content in soft drinks.
- To improve the **iron** content in bread.
- To replace sugar in low sugar recipes.
- To allow the removal of fat from products.

The control of additives

The use of additives is controlled by the Food Act of 1984 which forbids the addition to food or drink of any substance which may be harmful to health.

All additives undergo rigorous research before they are awarded an 'E' number which shows EU (European Union) approval. Additives recognised as safe by the British Government, but not by the EU, are given an identifying number but this is not accompanied by an 'E'.

Concern has been raised about the possible long-term effects of consuming large quantities of additives as so many of our foods now contain them. As a result of this concern, many manufacturers are striving to produce wholesome foods which contain fewer additives. These foods require different care and storage if they are to be kept in good condition.

Fig. 2.36 *Foods with fewer additives*

3 WORKING WITH INGREDIENTS

*Food products are made from a variety of ingredients (**components**). The ingredients chosen and the way they are mixed together allows different results to be produced. For example, whisking egg whites and gently folding them into a mixture of melted chocolate, sugar and egg yolks enables a light and fluffy chocolate mousse to be produced. Whereas, beating an egg and mixing it with milk creates a firm, set filling for a flan.*

The first important part of making successful food products is to choose the **right ingredients**. Basic recipes provide valuable information, such as which ingredients to use, the quantities required and how to make the mixture. Any dry flavourings, such as spices, should be added with the dry ingredients. Any moist or wet flavourings, like tomato puree or vanilla essence, should be added with the wet ingredients. This ensures that they are thoroughly mixed in.

Fig. 3.1 *The ingredients for a chocolate mousse*

When making food products it is important to **measure** all ingredients accurately. This ensures that the correct amount of each ingredient is present and that the ingredients are in the right **proportions** to one another. If this does not happen, the mixture will not be successful. Measuring can be done using various pieces of equipment such as scales, measuring jugs or spoons. Measuring temperatures is also important when working with some ingredients, for example, warm water is added to yeast.

Fig. 3.2 *Using a hand whisk can prevent over beating*

Ingredients can be **combined** (mixed) by hand or by using special equipment. Electrical equipment produces quick and consistent results. Hand mixing can also produce excellent results and is particularly useful when handling delicate mixtures, e.g. whisking double cream.

Food products can be **shaped** before or after they are cooked. The pastry is rolled, shaped and cut before sausage rolls are cooked. Swiss rolls are rolled up after cooking so that a cold filling can be included.

Temperature also plays an important part in producing food products. This may be by introducing heat (e.g. baking) or by removing heat (e.g. chilling or freezing).

Fig. 3.3 *An automatic bread maker bakes bread*

Hygiene and safety

Good **hygiene** *prevents food poisoning. Good* **safety standards** *prevent accidents.*

Hygiene is extremely important in the production of high quality food products. Good hygiene standards start with the cleanliness and careful dress of the person handling the food (see page 24) and continue with the preparation, cooking and storage of the food itself.

A safe working area is important because many dangerous pieces of equipment are used (e.g. sharp knives and electrically operated machines) often alongside hobs and ovens set at very high temperatures which, on occasions, can exceed 200°C. All sorts of injuries could occur in this environment so safe practices must be followed to prevent accidents.

The following hygiene and safety rules will ensure that food is prepared hygienically in a safe environment.

Fig. 3.4 *The rules of hygiene and safety*

Rule	Reason
Hygiene	
Cover hair with hat or net or tie hair back	To prevent hairs and dust falling into food
Remove jumper and tie and roll sleeves up	To prevent floppy clothes touching food
Wear clean apron	To prevent dirt and particles falling into food
Cover cuts with a plaster (blue if possible)	To keep wound clean and prevent blood from contaminating food
Wash hands before handling food, after blowing nose, touching face or hair or visiting the toilet	To ensure no bacteria are passed on to food
Clean work surfaces with anti-bacterial cleanser before use, e.g. Dettox	To remove bacteria on work surface
Wash all equipment, hands and work surface after preparing raw meats or vegetables	So bacteria from meat juices or soil are not transferred to food
Wash up in hot soapy water	So equipment is clean and all traces of food are removed
Store all high-risk foods (e.g. eggs, meat, milk) in fridge until required	To prevent growth of bacteria and food spoilage
If food is not to be eaten after cooking, cool and store in fridge until required	To prevent growth of bacteria
Do not put hot or warm food in the fridge or freezer	To prevent raising the surrounding temperature, which enables bacteria to grow
Store all clean equipment in drawers and cupboards	To keep it clean and prevent pest contamination
Keep rubbish separate when preparing food	So table is well organised and rubbish does not contaminate food
Empty bins daily	So pests are not attracted
Wash all cloths regularly with detergent in washing machine on very hot wash	So they are thoroughly clean and any traces of food are removed
Safety	
Cover hair with hat or net or tie hair back	To prevent hair getting caught in machinery and possibly catching fire on gas flame
Remove jumper and tie and roll sleeves up	To prevent floppy clothes touching gas flame or catching in machinery
Do not run in food preparation areas	To avoid falling over, bumping into people, hot liquid or sharp objects
Place all bags under tables or in allocated areas	To prevent tripping over
Do not touch electrical appliances with wet hands	To prevent electric shocks
Wipe up spills immediately	To prevent accidents
Do not leave knives or glass in washing up water	To prevent breakages and cuts
Carry knives with the blade facing downwards	To prevent cutting someone or stabbing self with tip
Turn saucepan handles to the side or back of cooker	To prevent accidentally catching handle or handle heating up over hob ring

Hygiene and safety in the food industry

In the food industry the importance of hygienic food preparation is particularly important. Many portions of food are prepared in one batch, and therefore lots of people can be made ill by one contaminated batch.

Food manufacturers are bound by law to ensure that they take the greatest of care in preparing food. The Food Safety Act 1990 is the main law which ensures that all foods, from raw ingredients through to products on the supermarket shelves, are safe for us to eat. There are certain people whose job it is to check that the food safety laws are being correctly carried out. They are called **trading standards officers** and **environmental health officers**.

Trading standards officers make sure that the information on packaging is correct, and that weights and measures are labelled accurately. This ensures that when we buy food products we cannot be misled by the food manufacturers.

'**Billion' cost of foul food**

Louise Jury

Food poisoning could be costing more than £1 billion a year, public health scientists said yesterday as the bug which has affected 40 people in Blackburn, West Lothian, was traced to a dairy bottling plant in the town

Fig. 3.5 *Stories about food poisoning often appear in the papers*

Fig. 3.6 *A Trading standards officer checks a weighing scale*

Environmental health officers visit food premises to ensure that the high standards of hygiene, as laid down by law, are carried out. If the standards of hygiene are not good enough, the firm will be directed to make immediate improvements. If the improvements are not satisfactory, legal action is taken and the business can be fined and closed down. The person responsible can also be imprisoned.

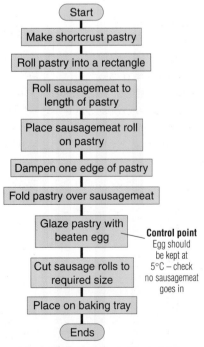

Fig. 3.7 *An environmental health officer checks the temperature of a meat counter*

Producing food products hygienically

Identifying a problem using HACCP (Hazard Analysis Critical Control Points)

Food manufacturers set up checking systems to ensure that all food is prepared hygienically. The first step is to look at every stage of making the product (**hazard analysis**) and then to identify areas where problems could arise (**critical control points**). For example, beaten egg may be used to glaze a pastry product. The raw egg is identified as a high-risk food because it provides favourable conditions for bacteria to grow.

Preventing the problem

Food technologists research ways to prevent these problems from arising and carry out **microbiological tests** to ensure that their planned system will work. For example, in the factory environment where the egg glaze is used the temperature is kept cold to prevent the growth of bacteria, and the production line is also cleaned down at regular intervals to remove any egg that has built up during a production session.

Start

Make shortcrust pastry

Roll pastry into a rectangle

Roll sausagemeat to length of pastry

Place sausagemeat roll on pastry

Dampen one edge of pastry

Fold pastry over sausagemeat

Glaze pastry with beaten egg — **Control point** Egg should be kept at 5°C – check no sausagemeat goes in

Cut sausage rolls to required size

Place on baking tray

Ends

* Ensure that production line is cleaned regularly

Fig. 3.8

Hygiene and safety in the classroom

Food poisoning is caused by:

- unclean working practices;
- incorrect storage;
- unhygienic conditions;
- incorrect cooking of foods.

It is very important to prevent bacteria transferring from hands, equipment or surfaces onto foods, and also from multiplying on foods, as this will cause food poisoning.

Bacteria require **warmth**, **food** and **moisture** to multiply. When these conditions are present, bacteria double in numbers approximately every 20 minutes. Bacterial growth slows down in cold temperatures such as a refrigerator.

Fig. 3.9 *Best before date*

Manufacturers carry out **microbiological tests** to check the bacteria levels in food. At school or at home, all food must be checked and correctly handled. Although it is not possible to detect bacterial activity in food just by using our senses, we do need to check that all our foods are of good quality. You can check that the colour is right and that the smell is as expected. Care needs to be taken to ensure that all **'best before'** and **'use by dates'** are accurately followed, as food is past its best after this time and could cause food poisoning (see page 79). Foods can be divided into two groups – **high-risk** and **low-risk**.

High-risk foods are generally high-protein foods (e.g. dairy products, raw and cooked meats and processed products), but they can also be cooked foods which provide moist, warm conditions (e.g. cooked rice). Bacteria flourish in these foods, so great care is required to ensure that they are stored in a fridge (below 5°C). They should not be kept in warm conditions for longer than absolutely necessary. Any made-up products that require cooking must be heated thoroughly to above 75°C to ensure that they are safe to eat.

Fig. 3.11 *Low-risk foods*

Fig. 3.10 *High-risk foods*

Low-risk foods (e.g. vegetables and dried foods) stay fresh for longer periods of time and can be stored at room temperature.

Processed foods are foods which have received some processing during manufacture, e.g. ready prepared meals, bread, fresh pasta or Pot Noodles. Once these foods are opened they must be treated as fresh foods.

1 List eight of your favourite meals or foods. Separate the ingredients used to make them into high- and low-risk foods. (Use recipe books to help you if you need to.)

2 Produce a table using the headings on Fig. 3.12 and fill in the information you have researched.

Transporting and storing food for school

When you need to take food to school for practical sessions you should always prepare it the night before. This enables you to be organised and not in a rush. Store any high-risk foods in the fridge or freezer and take them out as you leave for school. Remember to leave yourself a note so that you don't forget! *(Note – use an insulated bag or layers of paper to keep the food cold.)* When you arrive at school, store the food in the correct conditions as soon as possible.

Food	Storage	Reason
High-risk foods		
Raw meat and fish	Covered on a plate on bottom shelf of fridge or in a special fridge for raw foods	So juices do not drip onto other foods and prevent bacterial growth
Cooked meats	In a covered container on top shelf in fridge	To prevent contamination and bacterial growth
Yoghurt, cream, etc.	Keep in covered containers in fridge	To prevent contamination and bacterial growth
Eggs	Transport in egg box and store in fridge	To keep fresh
Low-risk foods		
Cereal foods, e.g. flour	Place in covered containers and store at room temperature	Safe to store at room temperature
Unopened cans of food	Store at room temperature	Safe to store at room temperature
Fruit and vegetables	Store at room temperature or in salad drawer in fridge	Safe to store at room temperature. Fridge keeps them fresh for longer

Fig. 3.12   43

Measuring ingredients

When preparing and producing food products all measurements have to be accurate if the end result is to be successful. Measurements are used to:

- weigh dry ingredients (e.g. flour);
- weigh or measure liquid ingredients (e.g. milk, water);
- set and check temperatures (e.g. oven or fridge);
- ensure cooking timings are correct;
- ensure size and length of products are correct;
- check pH value of a mixture.

There are two units of measure but the most often used is metric (e.g. grams, centimetres and millilitres). Some recipes use imperial measures (i.e. ounces, pounds and pints). It is very important that when a product is being prepared only one system is used. Mixing metric and imperial measurements will not produce a successful product.

All the foods we buy are weighed and labelled in metric measures so that our products are in line with the rules and laws laid down by the European Union.

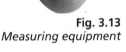

Fig. 3.13
Measuring equipment

Measuring dry ingredients

Dry ingredients are measured by weight in grams and kilograms. Alternatively handy measures can be made using spoons.

The measurements are:
Teaspoon = 5 g or 5 ml;
Dessertspoon = 15 g or 15 ml;
Tablespoon = 25 g or 25 ml.

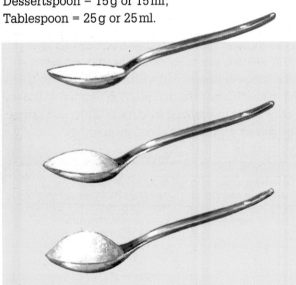

Fig. 3.14 *Level, rounded and heaped spoonfuls*

Measuring liquid ingredients

Liquids are usually measured by volume (i.e. millilitres and litres). Measuring jugs should be clearly marked so that accurate quantities are obtained. When measuring liquids you need to get your eye level with the measuring jug so that you can read the amount of liquid accurately.

Sometimes liquid quantities are required in spoonfuls. When this is required measurements should be taken from a container and not from a running tap so that an accurate quantity is collected. (See Fig 3.15).

Fig. 3.15

Spooning liquid out of a container will give you an accurate measure

Measuring temperature

Food production involves the use of temperature in many processes. It is generally measured in centigrade but in some instances a piece of equipment will have its own settings such as power levels on microwave cookers or numbers on dials for cooker hobs.

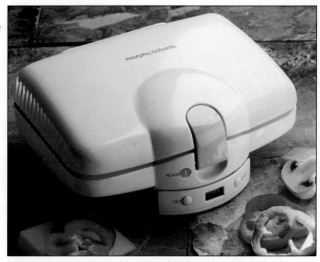

Hot temperatures are used to cook foods, such as on a hob, in an automatic bread maker or the different temperature zones in a gas oven. Cold temperatures are also important to ensure food is stored safely in a fridge or freezer, and when producing chilled or frozen products such as ice cream. Whichever methods are being used, accurate temperature control is extremely important for a successful outcome.

Fig 3.16 *Sandwich toasters cook food quickly at a high temperature*

Environmental Health Officers pay particular attention to ensure that the temperatures in foods are accurately controlled. Temperature control is very important to ensure food is safe and successfully prepared (see Figs 3.17–3.21).

Fig. 3.17 *Food must be stored below 8°C to keep it in good condition and prevent growth of bacteria. Frozen foods must be stored below –18°C*

Fig. 3.18 *Food needs to be cooked thoroughly so that it is safe to eat (above 75°C)*

Fig. 3.19 *Hot food must be kept above 63°C – heaters and special light bulbs ensure this happens*

Fig. 3.20 *Some products need to be prepared at the right temperature to obtain the correct consistency (e.g. Jam is boiled to a high temperature)*

Fig. 3.21 *Reaching the correct temperature is often necessary to ensure a successful end product (e.g. milk should be heated to 26–32°C to make cheese successfully)*

⚠️ Warm or hot food should never be put in a fridge or freezer.

Measuring length, size or quantity

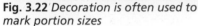

Fig. 3.22 *Decoration is often used to mark portion sizes*

The accurate measurement of **portion sizes** is essential if the correct number of products is to be made from a batch of mixture. It also ensures that an exact number of products will be made when several batches of mixture need to be produced in one go. Many pieces of equipment and techniques are available to allow portion sizing to be carried out with ease.

Fig. 3.23 *Accurate portion sizing is important to ensure that everyone gets the same sized product!*

Fig. 3.24 *Overfilled cake cases*

Recipes usually give a guide to the quantity each batch of mixture will **yield**. This needs to be followed accurately to ensure a successful result. For example, if 12 small cakes are made from a batch of mixture instead of the 18 stated in the recipe, the paper cases will be too full. This will result in the mixture rising and spilling over the paper case and will produce an unattractive and heavy cake. It also means that there are fewer cakes to go round or, in the business world, fewer cakes to sell! Alternatively, if more cakes are made than the stated 18, they will probably turn out to be very small, unrisen cakes because there was insufficient mixture in the paper cases.

On occasions, small, equal sized quantities of mixture need to be taken from one ball of dough, as when making cookies. The best way to do this is to shape the dough into a **long rectangle**, and then divide it into sections to achieve the number required. Each individual cookie may then be shaped into a ball, placed on a greased baking tray and gently pressed flat with a fork.

Fig. 3.25 *Cutting a mixture that has already been marked*

Fig. 3.26 *Bread dough being weighed and divided*

Alternatively, when a mixture needs to be divided up into large portions (e.g. if three pizza bases are to be made from one batch of bread dough), the dough can be divided by **weighing** out the number of portions required.

When a pastry or biscuit mixture needs to be rolled out to a **consistent thickness**, objects of the required depth can be used as a guide. For example, clean plastic rulers, which are kept only for food production purposes, can be placed alongside the dough when it is being rolled out to ensure an even and consistent result. Care must still be taken to ensure that the dough is moved between rollings to ensure it does not stick to the surface.

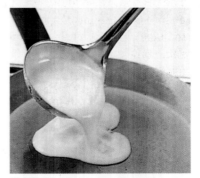

Fig. 3.27 *Liquids can be easily measured with a ladle*

Measuring the acidity of a mixture

All foods are made up of a variety of natural **food chemicals**. The type and amount of food chemicals present in the food create **acidic**, **alkali** or **neutral** conditions. Food investigations can be carried out to discover which group a particular food belongs to.

Fig. 3.28 *A range of acidic foods*

The **acidity level** of foods can be measured with special papers which are impregnated (filled) with chemicals. The paper changes colour depending on whether the conditions are acidic, neutral or alkali. The colour is then compared against a chart and the level of acidity is identified. This acidity level is the food's **pH value**. A value of 7 means it is neutral (see Fig. 3.29).

A **probe** is an easier and more suitable way to test the pH value of a some mixtures.

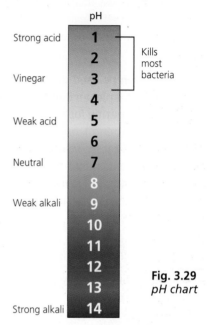

pH

	pH	
Strong acid	1	Kills most bacteria
	2	
Vinegar	3	
	4	
Weak acid	5	
	6	
Neutral	7	
	8	
Weak alkali	9	
	10	
	11	
	12	
	13	
Strong alkali	14	

Fig. 3.29 *pH chart*

Electronic sensors can also be used to measure pH values. They are used to ensure that the pH value of each batch of mixture is consistent so that the product will always taste the same, e.g. in yoghurt production

Fig. 3.30 *Yoghurt is tested for pH*

It is important to know the acidic level of foods because this can affect the end result of a product. For example, fresh fruits are quite acidic. If fruits are to be mixed into a milk product, the acid in the fruits can cause the mixture to **curdle**. Curdling causes the mixture to separate and become lumpy. Knowing what causes this to happen enables a food technologist to take steps to prevent it.

The pH value also affects the taste of a food, e.g. in tomato juice. To ensure that the taste of a product is always the same, care is taken to make sure that particular ingredients are always used, e.g. the same type of tomatoes. This may mean that several suppliers are used to ensure an all-year-round supply. When the tomatoes arrive at the factory careful checks will be carried out to make sure the quality of the tomatoes is high and that they satisfy all the specification requirements and that their pH value is correct.

On occasions **acidity regulators** may be required to ensure that the correct pH value is produced in the product. Lemon juice may be used to fulfil this function in school.

Fig. 3.31 *A curdled mixture*

Combining and binding ingredients

Individual ingredients (components) need to be properly combined if successful end products are to be produced. Some ingredients can be mixed together easily because they have similar consistencies (e.g. flour and dried spices, or beaten egg and vanilla essence). Others need more active mixing to become combined because they have very different consistencies (e.g. flour and margarine, or caster sugar and egg white).

Equipment can be used to make combining ingredients easier. For example, an electric mixer can be used to mix sugar and margarine for a cake mixture (this process is known as 'creaming'), or a liquidiser can be used to combine liquid and vegetables into a puree for a soup. Such equipment also enables consistent results to be achieved because it can be used on controlled settings and with exact timing.

Fig. 3.32 *Sugar and fat creamed in a food processor*

Methods of combining

You can combine ingredients by:

- **stirring** to mix them evenly (e.g. when adding chocolate chips to flavour a cake mixture);
- **folding** them into a mixture (e.g. flour into whisked egg white and sugar to make a whisked sponge).

Some methods of combining involve processes that enable other important functions to be carried out at the same time. For example, when margarine and sugar are beaten together air is incorporated which causes the mixture to rise when it is baked. Other processes that introduce air into mixtures include:

- **sieving** dry ingredients (e.g. flour, baking powder and spices);
- **creaming** margarine and sugar (e.g. to make a sponge cake);
- **whisking** (e.g. to make meringues);
- **rubbing** fat into flour (e.g. to make shortcrust pastry or scones);
- **folding** layers (e.g. to make flaky pastry).

Methods of binding

Binding holds ingredients together. You can bind ingredients together by adding:

- **liquid** to introduce moisture to hold dry ingredients together such as adding milk to a scone mixture;
- **beaten egg** to increase moisture to hold and shape ingredients for example, egg is added to minced beef, onion and breadcrumbs to make beefburgers.

Fig. 3.33 *Methods of combining*

Combinations of ingredients

Several major groupings of ingredients are combined to produce food products.

Liquid and starch (such as milk and flour) are combined when making batters and also used when thickening liquids.

Batter	
Yorkshire pudding/ pancakes/ toad-in-the-hole	
Milk	250 ml
Flour	100 g
Eggs	1–2
Salt	1/4 g

Fig. 3.34 *Pancakes*

Liquid and fat (such as vinegar and oil) are combined when making salad dressings.

French dressing	
Vinegar or lemon juice	15 ml
Vegetable oil	30 ml
Dry mustard	1/2 g
Sugar	pinch
Salt and pepper	pinch

Fig. 3.35 *Salad dressing*

Liquid and sugar (such as water or milk and caster sugar) are used to make syrups for fruit salads and to glaze sweet yeast mixtures such as hot cross buns.

Fig. 3.36 *Glazing*

	Fruit salad syrup	Glaze for sweet yeast mixtures
Water	250 ml	–
Milk	–	50 ml
Sugar	100 g	40 g

Fat and starch (such as flour and margarine) are combined when making plain cakes, biscuits and sauces.

Fig. 3.37 *Choux bun*

	Biscuits	Roux sauce (coating)
Margarine	75 g	25 g
Flour	200 g	25 g
Milk	–	250 ml
Sugar	75 g	–
Egg	1	–
Salt	pinch	to season

Fat and sugar are combined when making rich cake mixtures, by the creaming method and flapjacks by the melting method.

Fig. 3.38 *Flapjacks and shortbread*

	Rich cake mixture	Flapjacks
Margarine	100 g	50 g
Sugar	100 g	50 g
Flour	100 g	–
Rolled oats	–	125 g
Eggs	2	–
Golden syrup	–	30 ml

Binding
Dry ingredients (such as flour, or meat and seasoning) can be combined by binding them together using milk, water or egg.

Fig. 3.39 *Egg can be used to bind the ingredients in a beefburger*

	Hamburgers	Scones
Egg	1/2	–
Milk	–	125 ml
Minced beef	250 g	–
Onion	1	–
Flour	–	200 g
Margarine	–	25 g
Salt	1/4 g	1/2 g

Combining ingredients – liquid and starch

When liquids and starch are mixed together and heated, the mixture will thicken.

Fig. 3.40 *A variety of starches and ready-prepared thickeners used in food preparation*

Types of liquid and starch mixtures

A variety of liquids and starches are combined to produce many different food products. Some basic starch products are plain flour, cornflour and arrowroot. These are used to produce:

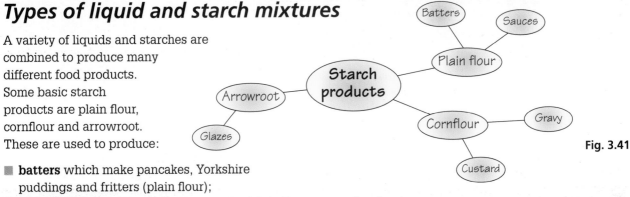

Fig. 3.41

- **batters** which make pancakes, Yorkshire puddings and fritters (plain flour);
- **sauces**, e.g. cheese, mushroom, parsley (plain flour or cornflour);
- **custard** (cornflour);
- **gravy** (cornflour);
- **glazes** which produce transparent (see-through) toppings for fruit flans (arrowroot).

Many part-prepared products are also available which require only a small amount of preparation, e.g. custard powder, blancmanges and gravy powder only need liquid to be added to produce the final product.

Some starches are **modified** (processed) which enables thickening to take place without further cooking. For example, gravy granules only require boiling water to be added and the mixture will thicken. Thickening granules can be stirred directly into hot food to thicken the liquid without lumps forming.

All of these mixtures require **heat** to thicken.

Other modified starches allow thickening to take place when a cold liquid is added. No heat is required for the thickening process to take place. An example of this is Angel Delight.

Fig. 3.42 *Angel Delight*

Choosing between liquid and starch mixtures

The type of starch chosen depends on the required finished result. For example, if a cheese sauce is being produced to coat cauliflower cheese, plain flour would be used as it produces a thick, **opaque** consistency which also adds colour to the finished product.

If, however, the product is a fruit flan which needs a glaze, the finished result needs to be transparent so that the fruit can still be seen. In this case arrowroot is the best starch to use.

Fig. 3.43 *Cauliflower cheese and glazed fruit flan*

Functions of liquid and starch mixtures

- They combine to produce thickened mixtures.
- Modified starches combine easily with liquids.
- When heated, some liquid and starch mixtures thicken and become transparent.
- Different consistencies of mixture can be produced depending on the proportions used.

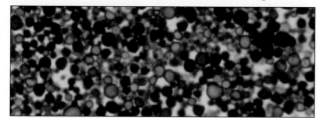

Fig. 3.44 *At 60°C liquid is absorbed by the starch. The particles soften and swell to up to five times their original size*

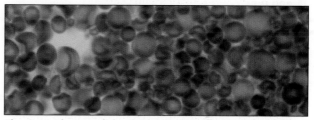

Fig. 3.45 *The starch has gelatinised (a gel has formed). When cool the gel sets and the sauce becomes solid*

Quality control

If a liquid has been heated and is still not thick enough, unprocessed starches such as flour or cornflour should not be added directly to the mixture as the starch will immediately form lumps. Instead, the following steps should be followed:

1 Measure a small amount of starch into a small bowl. Cornflour or arrowroot is best.

Fig. 3.46

2 Add only enough cold liquid to form a liquid (depending on mixture being made) and mix well.

Fig. 3.47

3 Slowly add some of this mixture to the saucepan, stirring all the time.

Fig. 3.48

Fig. 3.49

4 Add more mixture until the required thickness is obtained. Allow for the mixture to reach boiling point before further mixture is added

Combining ingredients – liquid and fat

Liquid and fat do not mix together easily. If they are forced together by friction (e.g. by shaking), they will combine for a while. After a short time the fat will separate out again and form a layer on the surface of the liquid. Some ingredients will act as an **emulsifier** to hold the liquid and fat together. The emulsifier prevents the two ingredients from separating out again.

Fig. 3.50 *Salad dressing that has separated*

Types of liquid and fat mixtures

There are two types of liquid and fat mixtures, depending on which of the two foods is present in a larger quantity:

- water and oil;
- oil and water.

Liquids and fats are naturally present in some foods such as:

- whole milk;
- egg yolk.

Fig. 3.51 *Cream on the surface of a bottle of milk*

Fig. 3.52 *Egg yolk*

In some cases the fat separates out, as in milk. In other cases it is combined in a mixture, as in egg yolk.

Many food products involve the combination of liquids and fats:

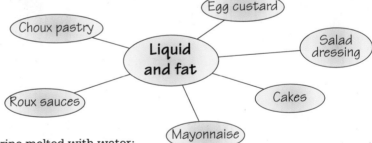

Fig 3.53 *Liquid and fat conbinations*

Choux pastry — Egg custard — Liquid and fat — Salad dressing — Cakes — Mayonnaise — Roux sauces

- **choux pastry**, e.g. eclairs – margarine melted with water;
- **roux sauces**, e.g. cheese sauce – milk added to a fat mixture;
- **mayonnaise** – oil and vinegar combined;
- **salad dressing** – salad oil and vinegar combined;
- **egg custard** – egg and milk beaten together;
- **cakes**, e.g. Victoria sandwich cake – egg and margarine beaten together.

Choosing a liquid and fat mixture

Now that most people are adopting a healthier approach to eating, we can buy many 'low-fat' varieties of products which are made up of liquid and fat mixtures. For example, low-fat mayonnaise, salad dressings and margarines are on sale in most supermarkets.

Fig. 3.54 *Low-fat and very low-fat margarines*

New processing techniques have enabled low-fat foods to be developed. One example of this is the wide variety of low-fat spreads now available. As these products contain high quantities of liquid, however, they are not suitable for use when baking cakes or pastries.

Cream is available in various forms which are useful in food preparation. **Single** cream is a mixture of milk and cream. It is used to enrich soups and sauces. **Double** or **whipping** cream contains a higher proportion of fat and can be whisked and piped as a decoration on a variety of desserts. **Clotted** cream is extremely thick and is eaten as an accompaniment to other foods, e.g. with scones and jam in cream teas.

Fig. 3.55 *Single, whipping, double and clotted cream*

Functions of liquid and fat mixtures

- Liquid and fat combinations require an emulsifier to produce a stable mixture.
- They combine to produce steam in baked products.
- They are used to produce low-fat spreads.
- Fat prevents baked products from going stale.

Fig. 3.56 *Liquid and fat will not combine without an emulsifier*

Quality control

Mixture	Quality check	Control point
Cake making (creaming method)	Make sure egg is at room temperature.	If margarine/sugar and egg mixture curdles, add 1 tsp flour.
	Make sure fat and sugar are creamed until light and fluffy.	
	Make sure egg is added gradually.	
Mayonnaise	Make sure mixture is not too thick.	Add vinegar until correct consistency is achieved.
	Make sure mixture is not too thin.	Add oil until correct consistency is achieved.
Roux sauces (e.g. cheese sauce)	Make sure margarine melts over low heat. Add flour and stir over heat.	Do not allow to burn.
	Do not allow to brown or flavour will spoil.	
	Gradually add liquid over gentle heat so it is more readily absorbed.	If lumps form, beat to remove them before adding more liquid. If *small* lumps remain, sieve and press lumps through. Bring to boil before serving.

Note: Full-fat milk can be replaced with semi-skimmed or skimmed milk to produce a healthier product without spoiling the overall result.

Combining ingredients – liquid and sugar

Sugar is very soluble in liquids. In its finest form, icing sugar dissolves easily in cold water. However, larger sugar crystals must be heated gently to enable them to dissolve. The larger the crystal, the longer it takes to dissolve.

Fig. 3.57 *Sugar has many uses in food preparation*

Types of liquid and sugar mixtures

Liquid and sugar solutions are used to produce mixtures with many different textures and appearances. A variety of mixtures can be obtained through combining liquids and sugars which do not require heating.

The simplest liquid and sugar solution is **glacé icing**. This is produced by adding cold water to icing sugar. It is used to decorate cakes.

Royal icing is made from raw or dried egg white, water and icing sugar. The icing sugar is gradually beaten into the egg white to produce a glossy, soft icing which is spread on cakes for special occasions, such as Christmas cakes. Glycerine is added to ensure ease of cutting and to prevent the icing from breaking apart when sliced.

Fig. 3.58 *Cake decorated with glacé icing*

Meringues are also made from a liquid and sugar mixture. The meringue is whisked to form peaks and then caster sugar is added. This mixture can be used to produce crisp, dry meringues that are filled with cream or used as a topping on pies. Meringue is usually dried out in an oven set at a low temperature. If the meringues are to be cooked in a microwave oven, icing sugar should be used instead of caster sugar. This is because the meringues will cook so quickly that caster sugar would not have time to dissolve and sweeten the product.

Fig. 3.59 *Sugar caramelises when heated*

Sugar syrups are used in fruit salads, as glazes on baked products and in sweet-making. The type and amount of liquid and sugar used differ depending on how the syrup is to be used. If the solution continues to heat, it **caramelises** to produce a golden brown colour. Overheating will create a dark brown solution which is bitter to the taste.

Liquid and sugar solutions are also used to make syrups in which fruits are bottled and when making chutneys and pickles. Water is used when bottling fruit, but vinegar may be used when chutneys and pickles are being produced.

Fig. 3.60 *Chutney and pickles*

Sweets such as fudge and toffee contain the same proportions of liquid and sugar. However, the liquid used may differ. Fudge usually contains milk and toffee usually contains water. The temperature used for cooking fudge is lower than that used for toffee and this contributes to the difference in texture in the end result. Fondant icing is made using the same quantities and ingredients as toffee, but it is heated at a lower temperature. This makes the mixture supple so that it can be shaped.

Liquid and sugar solutions are used in jam-making. The quantity of sugar used is far greater than the quantity of water, although the other ingredients will release liquids as they are heated. Some recipes require reduced quantities of sugar so that they will be healthier. Once opened, these low-sugar products should be stored in the fridge to prevent the growth of micro-organisms.

Fig. 3.61 *Toffee and fudge*

Fig. 3.62 *Jam and a low-sugar alternative*

Choosing liquid and sugar mixtures

Many types of sugar are available in both white and brown varieties. White or brown sugars of a similar type can replace one another in many cases unless the colouring produced by brown sugar would be undesirable. The finest form is **icing** sugar which is used to make sweets and icings as they require a smooth texture. **Caster** or **soft brown** sugar can be used when making cakes and biscuits as they both dissolve in the oven temperature required for these products. Larger sugar crystals, such as **granulated** and **preserving** sugar, are used when longer, slower heat treatments are needed, as when making syrups and jams.

Functions of liquid and sugar mixtures

- They add **flavour** to a product.
- They can be used as a **preservative** as very large quantities of sugar prevent the growth of bacteria in a product.
- They add **moisture** to products, so preventing them from drying out, e.g. in fruit salads.
- They combine to produce **decorative icings** for cakes and glazes for pastry products.
- They are **major ingredients** in the basic mixture of many products.
- They become denser and will even **set** as a solid as the proportion of sugar increases.
- They add colour if heated to a high temperature.

Quality control

Mixture	Quality check	Control point
Glace icing	Too runny	Sieve in more icing sugar.
Meringue	Does not whisk into peaks	Some grease on equipment or white egg yolk in egg.
Jam	Crystals in mixture	Sugar not completely dissolved.

Fig. 3.63 *Sugar is needed in cakes and biscuits*

Combining ingredients – fat and starch

Fat and starch mixtures require processing to enable them to combine. They are the basis for many pastries, cakes and sauces.

Types of fat and starch mixtures

The simplest fat and starch mixture is a roux sauce. The fat is **melted** then the starch is added and the mixture is stirred over a low heat so that the starch granules burst. When the liquid is added over a low heat, it is absorbed more easily and fewer lumps will form.

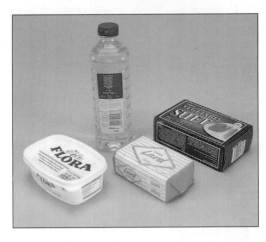

Fig. 3.64 *Types of fat*

Fig. 3.65 *Fat being rubbed into flour*

The fat may be **rubbed into** the starch if it is less than half the quantity of flour used. Crumbles, shortcrust pastry, scones and plain cakes (less than half the amount of fat to flour) are made using this method. A food processor can be used to carry out this process but care needs to be taken not to rub in the mixture too much.

If the quantity of fat is more than half of the quantity of the flour, the mixture is usually **creamed** or **melted** with other ingredients before the starch is added. The higher quantity of fat makes the mixture richer, so it lasts for a longer period of time before going stale. This type of mixture is used to make sponge cakes, rich fruit cakes and puddings. Electrically operated mixers are extremely good at carrying out this task without any effort from you. The starch should be **folded** in so that the air already beaten into the mixture does not become displaced, and to prevent a heavy, uneven texture.

Fig. 3.66 *Folding flour into a creamed mixture*

Choosing fat and starch mixtures

The fats and starches used will depend on what product is being made. **Butter** or **margarines** with at least 70% fat content are most often used in these mixtures.

Starches are available in different forms including wheat flour, cornflour and rice flour. A combination of starches may be used in some recipes. For example, some shortbread recipes state that a combination of plain and rice flour should be used to give the product a crumbly, melt-in-the-mouth texture.

Shortcrust pastry, plain cakes and biscuits require **plain** flour, while rich cakes need **self-raising** flour. Breads and all flaky pastries require **strong** flour as it provides the structure to hold the products up once they have risen.

Functions of fat and starch mixtures

■ They form the base for products such as cakes, biscuits and pastries.

■ When the flour particles are surrounded by fat this will shorten the mixture.

■ Fat is absorbed by the flour, creating air holes which lighten the mixture.

■ The mixture will thicken when heated.

■ Fat prevents cake and bread products from going stale.

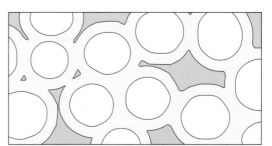

Fig. 3.67 *How the rubbed in method works – particles of flour are surrounded by fat*

Fig. 3.68 *It is important to use the right amount of flour*

When rolling out a fat and starch mixture it is important that limited quantities of flour are used to prevent the mixture from sticking to the work top surface. If too much flour is used, the flour will form a layer on the outside of the mixture. This will give an unpleasant floury taste and wll spoil the proportions and make the mixture dry up.

The mixture must also be cooked at the correct temperature if the product is to cook successfully. For example, if flaky pastry is not cooked at the correct temperature, the fat will not melt quickly enough to leave air pockets. This means that the pastry will not rise and a heavy, fatty pastry will result.

Fig. 3.69 *Well risen flaky pastry and biscuits use air to create the desired result*

Some products do not require the mixture to rise and therefore plain flour is used. For example, biscuits are made with plain flour which is sieved and the fat is then rubbed in. Both of these actions trap small amounts of air within the mixture which gives the product a light texture. If self-raising flour was used, the biscuit would not be flat, but would rise and would then not have the flat appearance required.

Quality control

Mixture	Quality check	Control point
Roux sauce	Floury taste	Continue cooking so that the starch granules burst and thicken the liquid.
	Greasy texture	Ensure all ingredients are accurately weighed.
Biscuits	Biscuits have risen	Use plain flour, roll mixture thinly and prick with a fork.
	Over rubbed in mixture forming lumps of greasy mixture	Add a little more flour, very lightly rub in and carefully add liquid to achieve correct consistency.
Flaky pastries	Not risen	Ensure oven temperature is at correct setting.
Pastries and biscuits	Floury taste	Use small amounts of flour when rolling out Ensure oven temperature is at correct setting.

Combining ingredients – fat and sugar

Fat and sugar combine together well. The sugar allows air to be taken into the mixture as it is beaten. When the mixture is cooked the trapped air causes the mixture to rise. A well-beaten mixture turns pale, which shows that there is air in it.

Fig. 3.70 *A well-beaten mixture turns pale*

Types of fat and sugar mixtures

Fat and sugar mixtures are most often used in the baking of rich cakes. The sugar chosen is usually a fine-sized crystal. **Caster sugar** or **soft brown sugar** are usually the most successful in these mixtures. This is because they dissolve easily in the hot oven during the time it takes for the product to cook. Larger sugar crystals would not dissolve completely which will affect the flavour and give a crunchy texture to the product.

There are two ways in which rich cake mixtures can be made.

The **traditional method** is to cream the fat and sugar until it is light and fluffy. Egg is added gradually and beaten in and then the flour is gently folded in. Most cooks believe that this method is the best, although it takes longer.

Fig. 3.71 *A cake made by the all-in-one method*

1. Measure sugar and butter or margarine into a bowl. Beat together.

2. Add lightly beaten egg a little at a time

3. Sieve and fold in flour

Fig. 3.72 *The stages of the traditional creaming method*

The second method, which was developed when soft margarines were first introduced, is the **all-in-one method**. All the ingredients are placed in a bowl and beaten until a soft, dropping consistency is achieved.

In both methods the side of the bowl is scraped down to ensure that all the ingredients are carefully mixed in.

1. Measure ingredients and add to bowl.

2. Beat ingredients together

3. Check that a soft, dropping consistency has been reached

Fig. 3.73 *The stages of the all-in-one method*

Butter icing is a fat and sugar mixture which is used to decorate cakes and gateaux. It is beaten to mix the ingredients thoroughly and to include air which adds bulk to the mixture. The icing sugar needs to be sieved onto the fat so that no lumps get into the mixture. Traditionally, the proportion of fat is half the amount of the icing sugar, but less fat can be used.

This mixture is firm enough to spread or pipe using a variety of nozzles to achieve different effects.

A wide range of flavours such as chocolate, coffee or lemon can be used in this mixture and small amounts of food colouring can also be used to make it more attractive. Food colouring should be measured into a clean teaspoon so that only the required amount is used.

Fig. 3.74 A cake decorated with piped icing

Choosing fat and sugar mixtures

The type of fat used is a matter of personal choice in most cases. Butter was traditionally used, but these days, for health reasons, most people are trying to eat less animal fat and now sunflower margarine is more popular in this type of mixture.

There are several types of margarine to choose from. **'Block'** margarine cannot be used straight from the fridge as it is too hard. It needs to be taken out of the fridge some time before it is used so that it will soften.

Soft or 'tub' margarine can be used straight from the fridge as it has been whipped to a softer consistency during manufacture.

'Low-fat' varieties are unsuitable for baking. This is because some liquids have been added to the

Fig. 3.75 Types of fat used in cooking

margarine during manufacture. This margarine will not allow baked products to rise and therefore produces a heavy, close texture which is unpleasant to eat.

Functions of fat and sugar mixtures

- High quantities of sugar mixed with fat create a soft texture when cooked but will become firm when cooled.
- Well-beaten fat and sugar mixtures incorporate air which enables the product to rise during cooking.
- Fat and sugar mixture sweeten products.
- They can be used to decorate products.

A well-beaten fat and sugar mixture incorporates a large amount of air. This can be demonstrated by placing a sample of the mixture in a container of water. If it is well beaten, the mixture will float. If it has not been beaten enough, the mixture will sink.

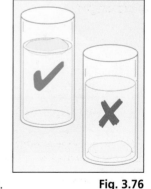

Fig. 3.76

Quality control

Mixture	Quality check	Control point
Rich cake mixture	Heavy texture	Beat mixture more thoroughly. Ensure oven is at correct temperature.
	Texture uneven with large holes	Beat fat and sugar mixture more thoroughly. Fold flour into mixture.
	Cake has risen to a peak	Oven too hot. Placed too high in oven. Too much mixture in container.
Butter icing	Tastes too much of fat	Not enough flavouring added. Ensure ingredients are accurately weighed.
	Lumps of icing sugar in mixture	Sieve icing sugar into margarine.

Binding agents

A **binding** ingredient is used to hold a mixture together which would otherwise fall apart. A typical mixture may be made up of a large quantity of dry ingredients, such as a rubbed-in mixture of flour, margarine and sultanas to make scones.

Another type of mixture may contain some moisture but not enough to hold it together during cooking. A typical mixture of this type may be minced beef, onion and breadcrumbs to make beefburgers.

Fig. 3.77a *Scones need liquid to hold dry ingredients together*

Fig. 3.77b *Meatballs need egg to stop them breaking up when cooked*

Types of binding mixtures

Liquid

Many liquids are used to bind mixtures together.

Mixtures which are made up of low quantities of fat and high quantities of fine dry ingredients require a binder. In its simplest form this may be:

■ water;   ■ milk;   ■ egg.

This would be used in shortcrust pastry and scones. The liquid moistens the flour particles and creates a structure which binds the pastry together. This is then baked to form a crisp texture.

Fig. 3.78 *Water is added to pastry breadcrumbs*

Fig. 3.79 *Beaten egg is added to beefburger to bind the ingredients*

When a mixture is made up of larger pieces of food, as in a beefburger, a binding ingredient is needed which will hold all the different parts together. Beaten egg will do this as it **coagulates** (sets) when heated. Egg can also be used to bind and enrich mashed potato used in fish cakes to make them keep their shape.

Starch

Starch, in the form of flour, can also be used to bind together a moist mixture of mashed potato which may be used in fish cakes. The flour absorbs some of the moisture and binds and firms it so that it can be shaped.

Mayonnaise

Mayonnaise is also used as a binder when it is mixed with ingredients such as mashed hard-boiled egg. It holds the mixture together so that it can be used as a filling in sandwiches. The mayonnaise prevents the filling from falling out.

Fig. 3.80 *Starch will help fish cakes to keep their shape*

Margarine and golden syrup

The combination of **margarine** and **golden syrup** binds dry ingredients, such as biscuit crumbs for cheesecake bases. The margarine is melted with the golden syrup and then the biscuit crumbs are carefully folded in. The mixture is then put into a greased container and pressed down firmly. As the margarine sets, it binds the crumbs together so that the cheesecake can be cut and the base will hold together without breaking up.

Fig. 3.81 *Biscuits being mixed into margarine*

Another mixture which also successfully binds dry ingredients together as they set is a **syrup** mixture. The dry ingredients are mixed into the syrup mixture and shaped into clusters as required. As the mixture sets and hardens, the dry ingredients are firmly bound together.

Fig. 3.82 *Flapjacks*

Liquidising

A mixture which is made up of a large quantity of liquid and pieces of vegetable can be liquidised to produce a smooth, thick mixture. This process also spreads fine particles of starchy ingredients throughout the liquid where they will act as a binder. The mixture will not separate out.

Freezing liquids

When liquids are frozen a network of ice crystals is formed. This process binds the mixture together by forming a solid, such as ice-cream.

Fig. 3.83 *Ice-cream contains a network of ice crystals*

Quality control

Mixture	Quality check	Control point
Scones, shortcrust pastry, fish cakes	Mixture too wet	Add a small quantity of flour until a firm dough is achieved.
	Mixture too dry	Add a small quantity of water or milk until a moist dough is achieved.
Ice cream	Large crystals	Ensure mixture is sufficiently mixed during freezing.
Beefburgers	Mixture falls apart	Ensure enough beaten egg is added and mixed in well. Ensure ingredients are chopped small.

Portion control

Manufacturers take great care to ensure that food products are accurately divided into portions. Consistent sizes are essential in the production of high quality products. If uneven-sized products are produced, they will cook unevenly and customers will complain!

Fig. 3.84 *Using scales to divide a mixture*

Fig. 3.85 *Portions should be as similar in size as possible*

In order to work out the cost of a number of products made from one batch of mixture each product needs to be a similar size. Trying to calculate the cost of small, medium and large portions all from one batch causes problems for manufacturers.

If consistent portion sizes are produced, accurate calculations can then be made about how many batches of mixture will be required to produce a set number of food products.

There are many ways in which food can be equally divided to ensure that consistent sizes are always achieved.

Food products in a **runny** or **liquid** form can be measured out into equal-sized portions using a variety of containers. For example, pancake mixtures can be portioned by using measuring jugs, spoons or ladles.

Foods which have a **soft consistency**, such as cake mixtures, may be measured by

using spoons to ensure the accurate division of the mixture. Alternatively, the weight of the mixture can be divided by the number of containers to be used.

Mixtures which have a **stiff consistency**, such as biscuits, scones and bread dough, can be shaped into a rectangle and portioned by dividing the rectangle into the required number of portions.

Fig. 3.86 *A rectangle of scone dough can be easily divided*

Alternatively, the mixture can be weighed and this weight divided by the number of portions to be made.

Fig. 3.87 *Using set containers*

Mixtures can also be portioned by using a **set container** for each product. For example, an individual mousse may be portioned by pouring the required amount of mixture into a plastic

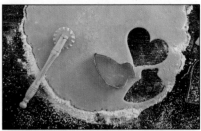

Fig. 3.88 *Using a cutter*

container to an agreed level. This would also ensure consistent size and pricing for each mousse.

Using a **set sized cutter** can also produce consistent sized portions and ensure a limited amount of waste.

Some products are produced in a large container and need to be divided into equal sized portions after cooking. This can be done in several ways but will require some measurement to ensure consistency. Batches of mixture, such as flapjack mixture, can be cut into different shapes.

On occasions some portions may be counted to ensure that consistent quantities are used. For example, pizza toppings, such as slices of tomato or green pepper, may be counted to ensure there is a consistent quantity of them on each product.

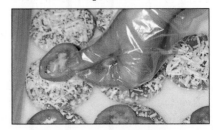

Fig. 3.89 *Counting tomato onto pizzas*

Shaping

Shaping is an important part of creating an attractive food product. It may be as simple as placing spoonfuls of mixture on a baking tray or using a mould or cutter which produces the required shape. More complex processes, such as making ravioli or putting lattice finishes on pastry products, also give a shaped finish which is functional (keeps the filling inside) as well as aesthetic (attractive to look at).

Shaping by hand

Some of the simplest forms of shaping are done by hand, such as shaping raw meat mixtures for **meatballs**. When the minced beef, breadcrumbs, seasoning and beaten egg have been thoroughly mixed, equal quantities of mixture may be shaped in the hands to form a round ball. The quantities used for each meat ball must be even if they are to cook fully in the same length of time. The meatballs are gently fried to seal in the juices and to obtain an attractive brown colour. They are then placed in an ovenproof dish to allow further cooking to take place in liquid.

Fig. 3.90 *Shaping meatballs*

Another simple form of shaping is done by placing spoonfuls of mixture on a baking tray. The mixture needs to be stiff so that it will not spread while cooking. An example of this is **rock bun** mixture which needs to be shaped in rough piles. When cooked the buns should be firm on the outside and have a soft texture inside.

Most cookie recipes produce a stiff mixture and some need to be shaped into a ball, placed on a greased baking tray and slightly flattened with a fork. This flattens the mixture evenly and leaves an attractive pattern on the surface.

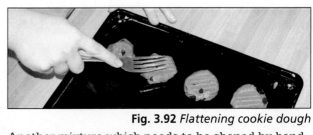
Fig. 3.92 *Flattening cookie dough*

Fig. 3.91 *Rock bun mixture being placed on a tray*

Another mixture which needs to be shaped by hand is **fish cakes** which contain cooled mashed potato. The cooked, flaked fish is mixed into the mashed potato and seasoned. The fish cakes are then shaped and coated in beaten egg and breadcrumbs to add texture and to make the appearance more attractive.

Bread doughs need to be shaped before they are finally proved and cooked. The mixture is kneaded thoroughly to obtain an even texture. After dividing the mixture equally, the dough needs to be kneaded once again to achieve a smooth finish and then shaped, e.g. into pizza bases, rolls and loaves. **Pizza bases** are often circles which are topped with a moist, tomato-based sauce or puree and a variety of different ingredients. **Bread rolls** may be shaped into rounds, plaits, horse shoes, cottage loaves, etc. They are then left to prove (double their size), glazed with beaten egg or milk and baked. **Loaves** are prepared in the same way as bread rolls. The dough may be put into loaf tins or prepared as large versions of the bread rolls.

Fig. 3.93 *Shaped breads*

Moulds

Shapes can be created by using a mould. Shortbread, cookies, jellies, chocolates and beefburgers are produced in this way. **Shortbread** and **cookie** moulds are lightly dusted with flour and then the mixture is pressed firmly into the mould so that the markings are impressed into the mixture. They are then turned out onto a baking tray and baked.

Fig. 3.94 *A mould for a savoury mouse*

Fig. 3.95 *Some moulds should be lined before you use them*

Jelly moulds need to be rinsed in cold water before the jelly is poured in so that it will come out easily when it is set.

Chocolate moulds need to be dry before the chocolate is poured in so that moisture will not discolour the chocolate.

Beefburgers can be made by placing a quantity of mixture in a round mould. A flat piece of plastic is placed on top and pressed down to level the mixture off evenly. The beefburger should not be too thick as it takes a long time to cook through to the middle and this can cause the outer layer to overcook.

Cream horns are made from strips of flaky pastry wound around a cream horn mould. The beginnings and ends of the pastry strips must be tucked under the mould so that they will not unwind when cooked. This also produces a neat finish on the top. The surface is brushed with egg white and dusted with caster sugar to add texture. Once cooked and cooled, the mould is removed and jam and whipped cream or other fillings are put inside the horns.

Fig. 3.96 *Beefburgers in a mould*

Fig. 3.97 *A cream horn*

Fig. 3.98 *Paper cases are disposable moulds*

A mould can also be used for making **pasties**. The base of the mould cuts out the pastry. The pastry round is then placed on the top of the mould. Filling is placed on one half of the mould and a small amount of liquid is brushed on the edges so that they will seal when pressed together. The two handles are then brought together and pressed gently to seal the edges and create a decorative finish. The handles are then gently opened and the resulting pasty placed on a baking tray. Different sized moulds are available.

Paper cases and all types of **cake tins** shape a product while it is cooking. The paper cases may be sweet size, bun tin size or larger muffin size. A variety of decorative shaped cake tins may be used, such as a clown's head, numbers or cartoon characters.

Fig. 3.99 *Cake tins shape food while it is cooking*

Shaping – rolling and folding

Rolling

Some recipes include rolling and folding in their production. The aim of rolling a mixture is to create an even, flat product, e.g. when making biscuits.

Other mixtures are used to line containers and hold fillings so they need to be pliable enough to shape. One example of this is shortcrust pastry which is used to line a container to make a savoury flan.

Fig. 3.100 *Rolling the biscuit mixture means the biscuits will be flat*

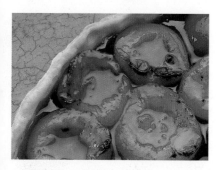

Rolling out mixtures allows many different types of products to be produced. The dough is transformed from a soft, moist mixture into a compressed layer which has a firm, crisp texture when baked.

Because of the pliable texture achieved from rolling, many different shapes can be produced from uncooked rolled out mixtures, such as shortcrust pastry folded into a semi-circle with fluted edges to make a Cornish pasty.

Fig. 3.101 *Shortcrust pastry is used to hold plums in this fruit tart*

Doughs can only be rolled out successfully if the ingredients have been accurately weighed. If there is too much of any one ingredient the proportions will be inaccurate and problems will arise. For example, if too much flour is used, the dough becomes dry and cracks when rolled out. If too much water is added, the dough becomes sticky. To ensure rolled out mixtures do not stick to the work surface, a light dusting of flour is required when rolling out.

Fig. 3.102
Cornish pasties

Successful rolling should be:

- done in short, sharp rolls so that the dough is not stretched too much;
- turned regularly to ensure it will be easy to lift when the correct thickness is achieved;
- left for a few minutes before use to allow it to relax in order to prevent shrinkage when the product is baked.

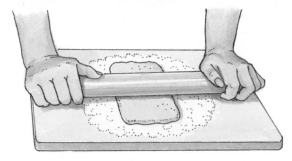

Fig. 3.103 *How to roll dough correctly*

Folding

Folding rolled out mixtures is easy if the mixture is the correct thickness. If the mixture is too thick, it may crack where it is folded, and too much pastry will also spoil the product. If it is too thin, it might tear when it is folded over a filling or shaped into a container.

Filo pastry is paper thin and several layers will need to be used to make it strong enough to hold fillings. Melted butter or margarine is used to moisten each layer so that it sticks to the previous layer. Because filo pastry is so thin, decorative parcels can be produced without thick layers of pastry building up where all the pastry is gathered to make the parcel shape.

Pastry can also be used to make decorative folds of pastry toppings on products.

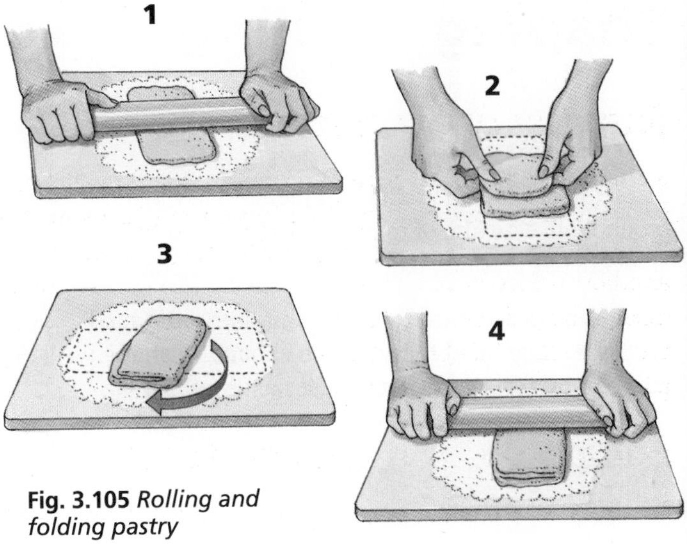

Fig. 3.105 *Rolling and folding pastry*

Fig. 3.104

Rolling and folding mixtures allows air to be trapped in the layers created by the folding process. All edges need to be sealed to prevent the air escaping. Rolling and folding is usually done to pastries which contain high quantities of fat. This type of pastry is cooked in very high oven temperatures. This causes the fat to melt quickly and become absorbed by the flour. The fat is absorbed by the flour leaving air spaces. The air expands when heated and the water in the mixture converts to steam which expands. This creates layers in pastry.

Pasta also requires rolling and folding. The mixture is thinly rolled and can then be used to produce many different types of filled and unfilled pasta. Any filling used needs to be dry otherwise problems arise when excess liquid prevents the pasta from sealing.

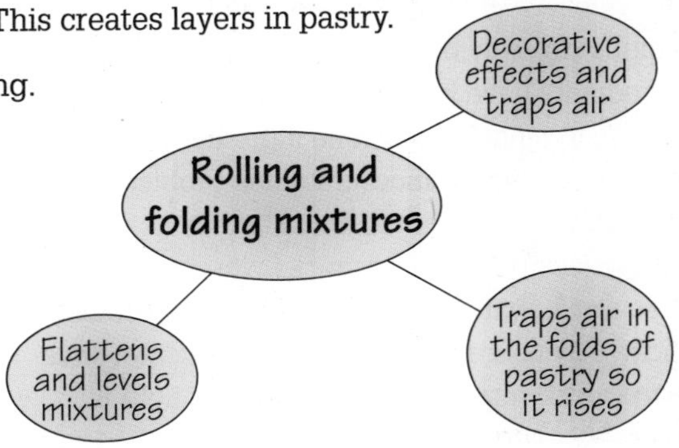

Fig. 3.106 *Making pasta*

Decorative effects and traps air

Rolling and folding mixtures

Flattens and levels mixtures

Traps air in the folds of pastry so it rises

Fig. 3.107 *Functions of rolling and folding mixtures*

Quality control

Quality check	Control point
Mixture too wet	Add liquid in teaspoon measures to prevent too much being added.
Cracks when rolled out	Do not over rub in fat to flour. Ensure weighing is accurate. Ensure correct amount of liquid is added.
Uneven rolling of dough	Ensure equal pressure is being used. Turn dough round when rolling to ensure even rolling and that dough does not stick to surface.
Pastry shrinks	Ensure short sharp rolls are used and pastry is left to relax before use.
Flaky pastry does not rise	Ensure folds are sealed to prevent air escaping.
Pastry joins come apart	Dampen edges of pastry with water so they stick together.

Shaping

Shaping using cutters

Some **cookie** or **biscuit mixtures** may need to be rolled out and the shapes cut out using shaped cutters. The cutters may be plain round, fluted or more complex shapes. The shapes should be cut out very close to one another so that as many biscuits are cut out from the first rolling of the mixture as possible. These products are best as they have been handled the least. Also, the proportions of the ingredients can be spoilt by the addition of extra flour required for rolling out the mixture several times.

Equipment for shaping food

All of these items will give an attractive, fun appearance to food products.

A **melon baller** can be used to cut ball shapes from foods such as melon and raw potatoes.

Fig. 3.108 *A melon baller has been used to create an attractive item*

Fig. 3.109 *Using a piping bag*

Piping bags can be used to shape whisked cream, choux pastry, meringues and mashed potato.

Shaped cutters, which cut sections out of the top layers of biscuits, can add interest to the finished product. This is done by cutting out the same sized bases and tops and placing them all on a baking tray. Shapes are cut out of the top layers and they are all cooked. A layer of jam or something similar is spread over the bases and the tops are put on. The finished result is colourful as the jam shows through the shape cut out of the top of the biscuit.

Pie magic and **sandwich toasters** cook and shape food while it is cooking. The pie magic appliance shapes the pastry in the heated base and seals and shapes the lids of the pies. The sandwich toaster cooks and divides the toasted sandwich in two.

Casting

Casting is a term used to describe an edible layer or lining, usually on the outside of a product. A variety of different ingredients or components may be used for this purpose, e.g. chocolate used to make an Easter egg or shortcrust pastry used to line a flan ring.

Fig. 3.110 *Easter eggs are moulded in chocolate*

Pastry is used to line a variety of different containers. For example, shortcrust pastry may be used to line a flan ring to make a quiche Lorraine or lemon meringue pie. The pastry needs to be fitted carefully into the flan base without stretching it so that it does not shrink when cooked in the oven. Any excess pastry needs to be removed, by rolling a rolling pin over the top of the flan ring. This cuts off the pastry so that it is level with the top of the container.

Fig. 3.111 *Pastry is used as a base for lemon meringue pie*

If the pastry needs to be **baked blind** it must be cooked without a filling. To do this successfully, the base needs to be pricked with a fork first to allow any trapped air to escape without making the base rise. Greaseproof paper is then placed carefully on the pastry and weighted down with baking beans. After approximately 10 minutes of baking, the greaseproof paper and beans need to be removed so that the base can be returned to the oven and cooked through.

The filling for some flans is made with a whisking method. The eggs and sugar need to be whisked until a thick mixture is obtained. To check that the mixture is sufficiently mixed, draw a fork along the surface. It should leave a trail.

Fig. 3.112 *Baking blind*

The next stage is to fold in the flour carefully so that as few air bubbles as possible are burst. If the flour is mixed in roughly many air bubbles will burst and the raising agent will be lost. Care should also be taken to ensure that no pockets of flour are left in the mixture.

The flan container must be well greased and dusted with flour to allow the flan to be removed easily when baked.

Biscuits can also be used to line containers, e.g. when making chilled cheesecakes. The biscuits are crushed and mixed with melted margarine and golden syrup and then flattened to form a thin layer covering the base and sides of the container. The mixture needs to be pressed down firmly so that, when chilled, it will come out of the container in slices.

Brandy snap mixture can also be used to create a casting. Spoonfuls of the mixture are placed on a well-greased baking tray. When cooked they must be quickly moulded over a container. As the mixture cools it sets hard in the formed shape. The container is then filled with a variety of fillings to produce an attractive product.

Fig. 3.113 *This brandy snap basket is filled with mango and banana mousse*

Layers of **chocolate** can also be used to line containers. The best known products produced in this manner are Easter eggs. The finished product may be hollow or filled. A filled product is made in two halves and then filled when the chocolate has set. The halves are joined by applying a thin layer of chocolate to the rim of one half and placing the other half on it. As the chocolate sets the shells are firmly joined together.

Some cold desserts can also be made with a chocolate casting. The container is lined with several layers of melted chocolate and, when completely set, can be filled with a variety of fillings, such as strawberry mousse or a variety of prepared fruits, and topped with piped cream.

Fig. 3.114 *Chocolate cakes*

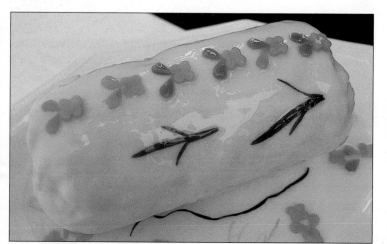

Aspic jelly or **sweet jelly** can also be used to line a container. If desired, decorations can be placed between two layers of jelly so that when the product is turned out onto a plate the decorations can be seen but cannot fall off the surface. Colourful decorations which contrast with the rest of the product, should be used to achieve the best results.

Fig. 3.115 *Carrot flowers have been stuck between layers of aspic to garnish this food product*

Fig. 3.116 *Bacon strips lined the container of this paté*

Fig. 3.117 *For fish dishes strips can be used to line a container in the same way as bacon*

Strips of uncooked bacon can also be used to line a container to create a decorative effect and to add flavour to the product. For example, when liver pate is prepared bacon is stretched slightly and layered to cover the sides and base of the container. After the filling is added more strips of bacon are placed over the top. After baking the product is turned out and served garnished with colourful foods. For fish products, containers are often lined with smoked salmon or other fish.

Yorkshire pudding can also be used to produce a casing. The cooked batter creates a case which can be filled with a variety of savoury fillings. Sweet fillings can also be used if desired.

Cutting by hand

Ingredients often need to be cut during the making of food products. A wide variety of basic equipment allows this tasks to be done easily.

Fig. 3.118 *A knife sharpener*

All knives should be kept sharp so that cutting can be carried out easily. Blunt knives require a lot of pressure when they are used and the knife can slip and cause an accident. A variety of knife sharpeners can be bought which can be used by hand or operated electrically.

Types of basic cutting equipment

Knives

A **cook's knife** has a strong, pointed blade approximately twice as long as the handle. It is used to cube, chop and slice a wide variety of foods.

Fig. 3.119 *A cook's knife*

A **bread knife** has a long blade similar to a cook's knife, but the cutting edge is serrated. This enables crusty loaves to be cut by a sawing action rather than through pressure which would squash soft bread.

Fig. 3.120 *A bread knife*

A **vegetable knife** is smaller than a cook's knife but also has a pointed blade. It is used to carry out more detailed tasks, such as trimming off unwanted sections of foods and slicing small fruits and vegetables.

Fig. 3.121 *A vegetable knife*

A **vegetable peeler** or parer is used to remove thin layers of skin from vegetables and fruits such as potatoes, carrots, pears and kiwi fruit. It can also be used to produce chocolate curls, but both the chocolate and your hands must be cold to prevent the chocolate from melting.

Fig. 3.122 *A vegetable parer*

Kitchen scissors have one plain cutting edge and one serrated cutting edge. They are useful for cutting thin or delicate foods, such as removing rind from bacon, cutting herbs into small pieces suitable for garnishing savoury products and for cutting pastry to create patterns.

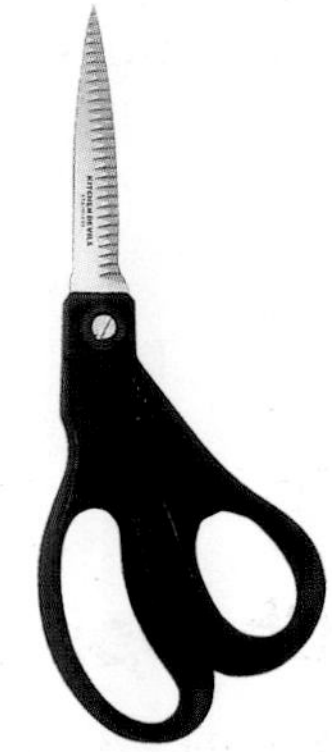

Fig. 3.123 *Kitchen scissors*

Graters cut food into smaller pieces. For example, a grater would be used to remove tiny pieces of the yellow rind of a lemon to flavour a product, or to produce coarse pieces of cheese to be melted on top of a pasta product. Most graters have coarse, medium and fine surfaces to enable a variety of sizes and thicknesses of food to be produced.

Fig. 3.124 *A grater*

Functions of basic cutting processes

There are many reasons why foods need cutting. It may be because:
- an ingredient is large and will not be cooked thoroughly if it remains its original size;
- the recipe requires the ingredient to be mixed with other foods;
- the food product may need to be cooked in a short time;
- the food product may need to be eaten as a snack;
- a small quantity of an ingredient may be required as a decoration or for flavouring.

There are many ways to cut foods. Each process has a special name. The correct name should always be used in recipes so that it is clearly understood what the end result will be.

■ **Chopping** – cutting into very small pieces.

Fig. 3.125 *Chopping*

■ **De-coring** – removing the core from a fruit, e.g. apple

Fig. 3.126 *De-coring*

■ **Dicing** – cutting into small cubes

Fig. 3.127 *Dicing*

■ **Grating** – using a variety of cutting edges to produce pieces of food of different sizes or thickness

Fig. 3.128 *Grating*

■ **Shredding** – slicing very thinly into very fine strips. The coarse cutter on a grater may be used for this with some foods

Fig. 3.129 *Shredding*

■ **Slicing** – can be done to achieve a variety of thicknesses depending on what the food is to be used for. Rings with a hollow centre are made by slicing some foods, e.g. onions or peppers.

Fig. 3.130 *Slicing*

Chopping boards

Always use the correct colour-coded chopping board as follows:

■ **white** – baked goods and dairy products;
■ **red** – raw meats;
■ **green** – salads and fruits;
■ **brown** – raw vegetables;
■ **yellow** – cooked meats;
■ **blue** – raw fish.

Quality control

It is essential to use the correct cutting process and to cut ingredients to the correct size to produce high quality products.

Note: If you need to remove segments of fruit from citrus fruits (e.g. an orange), no pith should be visible. To achieve this the skin should be cut off and the segments cut out.

Fig. 3.132 *An onion chopper*

Fig. 3.131 *Chopping boards*

> ⚠ Always carry knives with the blades pointing downwards. Always use a chopping board when cutting foods.

Cutting using mechanical and electrical equipment

Many mechanical and electrical devices are available which carry out a variety of cutting processes. Physical effort is needed to make mechanical pieces of equipment carry out their processes, e.g. when pressing down the handle of an onion chopper or when turning the handle on a pasta machine. These pieces of equipment are usually cheaper than electrical equipment.

Fig. 3.133 *A Mouli hand blender*

Mechanical equipment

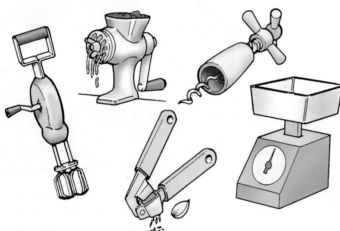

Fig. 3.134 *Mechanical equipment*

Mechanical equipment enables many awkward or time-consuming processes to be carried out easily with successful results each time. For example, a Mouli hand blender can be used to puree vegetables into a smooth paste.

Examples of mechanical appliances are shown in Fig. 3.134.

Electrical equipment

When using this equipment, electricity drives a motor which allows the process to be carried out with little or no effort from you. Electrical appliances are usually more expensive than mechanical equipment. The advantage of using electrical equipment is that consistent results will always be achieved if consistent speed settings and timings are used.

Sometimes the parts of the appliance which have been in contact with food are all removed for washing so that water does not come into contact with the electrical parts of the machine. On other pieces of equipment the flex is removed so that washing is easy. Otherwise the flex and machine may stay intact when washing is carried out. In this case, special care needs to be taken to ensure water does not come into contact with the plug or any parts of the motor as this can cause an electric shock which could be fatal.

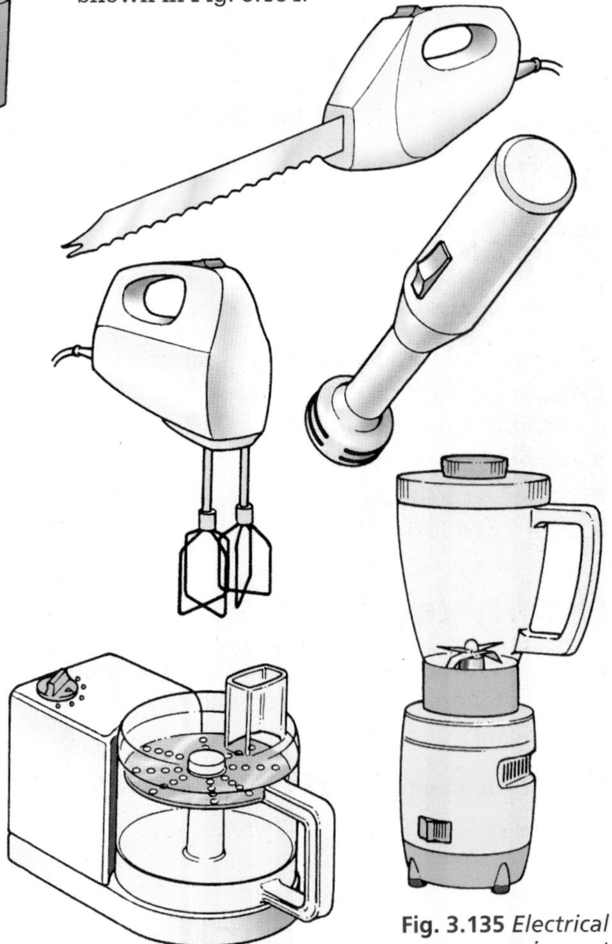

Fig. 3.135 *Electrical equipment*

The simplest electrical equipment includes:
- an **electric knife** which can cut thin slices of food (e.g. meat), and through frozen foods
- a **free-standing liquidiser** which can make crumbs from bread or biscuits and also puree soups and other foods.

Some small pieces of electrical equipment can carry out one or two processes. For example, a **small mixer** with a stand and liquidiser will whisk, cream, fold in and liquidise. This saves time and labour in food preparation. These machines are available at a reasonable cost.

Larger pieces of equipment are available in the middle to high price ranges but are a worthwhile investment if they will be used a lot in food preparation. A **large mixer** can carry out a number of processes using a variety of different attachments. For example, the cutting processes include grating, slicing, grinding, dicing, pureeing, chopping, potato peeling, mincing, extracting juice and liquidising. Other processes carried out by a large mixer include beating, whisking, folding in, creaming, kneading and extracting juice.

Fig. 3.136 *A Kenwood chef and its attachments*

Fig. 3.137 *A food processor and its attachments*

Food processors are available in a variety of sizes and with a variety of attachments. The price range varies depending on the extra attachments available and the size of the bowl and motor. Many food processors carry out similar tasks to a large mixer. The cutting processes include chopping, grating, slicing, dicing, chipping and liquidising. With most models it is also possible to whisk lightweight ingredients such as cream and egg whites.

 ■ Electrical appliances should never be touched with wet hands.
■ The flex or plug should not come into contact with water.

Heating

The aim of cooking food is to produce products which:

- have an attractive appearance;
- have good colour;
- have good flavour;
- have good texture;
- are easy to digest;

- are safe to eat;
- are easy to eat;
- have improved keeping qualities;
- provide hot food in cold weather.

Cooking depends on heat being transmitted through the food to cook right through to the centre. The amount of heat and the length of cooking time required depend on the food being cooked and the cooking method chosen.

Heat is transmitted to food by the following methods:

Conduction is when heat passes from **one molecule to another**, e.g. in shallow frying. By this method all food is cooked through to the centre.

Convection – the heat circulates in **air**, e.g. in boiling, deep fat frying, baking.

Radiation occurs when **heat rays** are transferred through the air to the food, e.g. grilling.

Radiation — Heat — Conduction — Convection

Fig. 3.138

Many pieces of equipment provide heat to cook food. Examples include:

- cooker with hob, grill and fan-assisted oven;
- microwave oven;
- multi cooker;
- contact grill;
- pie magic;
- pizza maker.

- doughnut maker;
- toasted sandwich maker;
- slow cooker;
- pressure cooker;
- automatic bread maker;

Fig. 3.139 An automatic bread maker, a deep fat fryer and an electric wok create heat to cook food

All food is cooked using either **dry** or **moist** heat but frequently these are combined.

The choice of cooking method used depends on the type of food being cooked, personal preference or dietary needs.

Dry cooking methods

Care needs to be taken to ensure that foods do not dry out during cooking. Delicate foods, such as white fish, will require only a short cooking time or they will become dry and tough. Larger, dense pieces of food, such as red meat, require longer, slower cooking to ensure that they are cooked thoroughly.

Grilling – Dry foods may be brushed with oil to prevent burning. The food needs to be placed on a grill rack so that fat will drip into the grill pan. The food should be turned regularly so that it is evenly cooked. The grill door must be left open to enable the food to be seen so that it does not burn. This method is suitable for thin, tender cuts of meat, chops, bacon, sausages, some fish, tomatoes and mushrooms.

Fig. 3.140 *Food being grilled*

Baking – Tins are greased to enable food to be removed easily when cooked. The oven temperature in a fan-assisted oven is the same on all shelves. In gas and non-fan-assisted electric ovens, the set temperature is on the middle shelf, with the shelf above being one setting higher, and the shelf below one setting lower. The oven must be pre-heated so that the temperature is correct and will enable the food to cook properly. Foods such as bread (oven temp. 200–220°C) and pastries (oven temp. 180–220°C) are cooked by this method.

Fig. 3.141 *Greasing a baking tin*

Roasting – The food needs to be brushed with oil to prevent burning. The oven temperature is set so that the food can be cooked through slowly to prevent it drying out. Special plastic roasting bags are available which prevent the food from drying out so that a more moist and tender product is achieved. If a roasting bag is not used, the food needs to be turned over about halfway through the cooking time to enable even cooking to take place. Meats and a variety of vegetables are generally roasted in a small amount of fat. The food is basted (brushed with fat) to prevent it drying out and to add flavour. (Oven temp. 180–200°C.)

Fig. 3.142 *Basting meat in a roasting tin*

Dry frying – This is usually done in a non-stick frying pan with a very small amount of fat. Pancakes and some stir-fry recipes are cooked by this method.

Fig. 3.143 *Cooking pancakes in a non-stick frying pan*

Microwaving – the microwaves create heat in food by agitating the molecules of moisture inside the food. As the heat transfers from molecule to molecule, it is passed from the outside of the food to the centre. Virtually all foods can be cooked by this method, but browning dishes or plastic bags may be required to produce attractive results. As food cooks quickly, care needs to be taken not to dry or burn foods cooked by this method.

Moist cooking methods

Moist cooking methods include a type of liquid with the food. The liquid may be in the form of fat, moisture produced during the cooking process or stock (water with onion or meat flavours). Milk may also be used, as when fish is poached, fruit juice is chosen to poach pears in. Wine, cider or beer can also be used to create different flavours.

The liquid should always be heated before the food is added to allow the food to start cooking immediately. A well-fitting saucepan lid should be used to prevent heat loss.

Boiling – The food is cooked in water at approximately 100°C. The bubbles should be rapidly breaking the surface of the water. Rice and pasta are cooked in this way. The rapid movement of the water prevents the particles of food from sticking together. The water should cover the food and reach approximately halfway up the side of the saucepan.

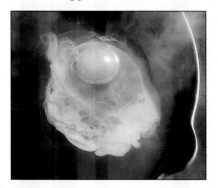

Fig. 3.144 *Spaghetti is added to boiling water*

Simmering – In this method bubbles are slowly rising and breaking on the surface. Potatoes should be cooked in this way so that they do not fall apart. The water should cover the food and reach approximately halfway up the side of the saucepan.

Poaching – Foods cooked by this method require very gentle cooking. The bubbles should rise gently to the surface with very little movement in the water. Delicate foods require this cooking method so that they will keep their shape and not fall apart. Poached eggs and fish are cooked in this way.

Fig. 3.145 *Poaching an egg*

Steaming – The food is cooked in the steam produced from boiling water. No water should touch the food. Food can be steamed:

- on a plate with a lid over it above a saucepan of boiling water;
- in a covered bowl in a saucepan of boiling water;
- in a tiered steamer.

It is important that all lids should fit tightly to prevent steam escaping. Care must be taken to ensure the saucepan does not boil dry. Boiling water should be on hand to top up the saucepan as the water level goes down.

Fig. 3.146 *Steaming vegetables in a tiered steamer*

Pressure cooking – The liquid inside a pressure cooker boils at a high temperature. The boiling point is increased because of the pressure.
The advantage of cooking this way is that it saves time and fuel energy as well as producing well-flavoured foods.

Fig. 3.147 *Using a pressure cooker*

Shallow frying – This method requires a small amount of fat to enable the food to cook. The fat needs to be heated before the food is added or the result is soggy, fatty food. A small piece of dried bread can be used to check if the fat is hot enough. If the bread sizzles the food can be added. The cooking food will need to be constantly checked and turned to prevent burning. As the temperature required to cook with fat is very high, great care needs to be taken. Fat should never be left unattended as it could burst into flames and cause a great deal of damage.

Fig. 3.148 *Frying bacon in a shallow frying pan*

Combining dry and moist cooking methods

Heat is first transferred to food by a dry method (such as dry frying) and then a moist method (such as casseroling) is used. This is often done because if meat is only cooked in a liquid the colour of the end product can be unappealing. To overcome this problem the meat can be browned in a little hot fat in a saucepan. Frying also adds flavour and seals in the juices so the end product tastes better. The food is then transferred to an ovenproof container and finishes cooking in liquid. The end result is a moist, tender food which is rich in flavour.

Fig. 3.149 *Casseroling meat*

Casseroling – This is used to cook foods such as meat with a variety of vegetables. Liquid is added to just cover the food. A tight-fitting lid is required to prevent the loss of liquid in the form of escaping steam. The vegetables and liquid are served with the meat.

Fig. 3.150 *Using a slow cooker*

Slow cooking – Casseroles are cooked in this container so meat has to be browned first in a pan on the hob. It is then placed in the heated slow cooker along with enough hot liquid to cover it. The meat simmers gently throughout its cooking time with the lid preventing any loss of liquid. The advantage of cooking this way is that the food can be prepared in the morning and left to cook throughout the day. It is then ready to eat when everyone returns home in the evening. This is a very economical method of cooking as it uses the same amount of electricity as a light bulb.

Fig. 3.151 *Cooking in a microwave oven*

Microwaving – Microwave ovens are very versatile appliances which can carry out a number of different tasks. Both dry and moist cooking methods can be done in microwave cookers. For example, minced meat can be cooked to seal in the juices and then liquid added to produce a bolognaise sauce. The spaghetti can also be cooked in a container of hot water, covered with pierced clingfilm to prevent the liquid from evaporating. Regular attention is required when food is cooked in this way. The recipe book that comes with the oven will give detailed instructions on cooking many different foods.

Chilling foods

The chilling process is a fairly new addition to the preservation techniques used to prolong the shelf life of foods. The type of foods which are preserved in this manner ideally need to be kept at temperatures of between 1° and 4°C. This prevents the growth of bacteria and moulds and allows the food to be safely stored in the fridge for a few days.

0°C
Water freezes

1–4°C
Fridge temperature;
bacteria grow slowly

5–63°C
Bacteria grow
quickly

121°C
All bacteria and
spores are killed

100°C
Water boils

−18°C
Bacteria are
not active

Fig. 3.152 *The growth rate of bacteria at different temperatures*

The types of foods which are found in the chill cabinet are dairy products, meat and fish, as well as many made-up products, such as lasagne, fresh pasta, pizzas, chilled soups, uncooked pastries and a variety of gateaux and cheesecakes. A wide variety of fresh snacks and sandwiches are also stored in these temperatures to ensure they are fresh and safe to eat.

Fridges must be kept clean and any spills wiped up as soon as possible. The fridge must be thawed or defrosted regularly if it is to work efficiently and run at the correct temperature. Foods need to be stored in the correct part of the fridge if problems are to be avoided.

Chilled foods must be transported from the supermarket and placed in the fridge at home as soon as possible. They should be carried in an insulated container during transportation to prevent the food from thawing. If the food is allowed to warm up, bacteria may grow and could cause food poisoning when eaten.

Fig. 3.153 *A well-stocked fridge*

If chilled foods need to be taken to school for practical sessions, they should either be transported in an insulated container or wrapped in several layers of newspaper to prevent the food from warming up.

Fig. 3.155 *Always read the 'use by' date*

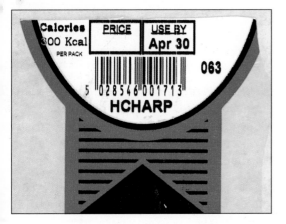

Fig. 3.154 *A variety of containers are available for transporting foods. If chilled foods are to be used place containers in a cool bag or wrap up with paper*

Once in the fridge chilled foods need to be rotated according to the 'best before' date so that the foods with the shortest shelf life are consumed first. **'Best before'** dates are usually given for foods with a short shelf life. **'Use by'** dates are used on less high-risk foods.

Freezing foods

Frozen foods can be stored for long periods of time because:

■ the temperature is too low for bacteria and moulds to grow and spoil the foods;
■ all the liquid is frozen solid so no moisture is available for bacteria to grow in.

Frozen foods need to be stored at temperatures between −18°C to −29°C.

They need to be quickly frozen to prevent large ice crystals forming in the cells. Large ice crystals cause the cells to become misshapen when they thaw again and so spoil the appearance of the food.

All foods should be chilled before being frozen so that they will freeze more quickly and not raise the temperature in the freezer. They should also be wrapped in freezer bags or plastic film or placed in airtight containers. This prevents the food from drying out or transferring smells and flavours to other foods in the freezer. The foods should then be placed in the rapid freeze section of the freezer to ensure they are frozen quickly.

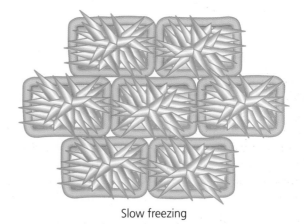

Slow freezing

Quick freezing – less damage is caused as the ice crystals are smaller

Fig. 3.156 *Ice crystals in frozen food*

Some foods, such as strawberries and raspberries, may be frozen loose so that their shape is kept intact. In this case the fruit is placed on trays and put in the rapid freeze section of the freezer. Once frozen, they can be packed in containers for storage. When required, the frozen fruit should be put on trays again so that they will thaw individually and keep their attractive appearance.

Many types of foods can be frozen although they may keep safely for varying lengths of time. Foods such as fish and meat products, pastries, gateaux, fruit and vegetables can be frozen successfully, as well as some milk products and ready prepared products which require very limited preparation before cooking.

Fig. 3.157 *A well-stocked freezer*

*	*Frozen food may be stored for one week*
**	*Frozen food may be stored for one month*
***	*Frozen food may be stored for three months*

Fig. 3.158 *Frozen food symbols*

A rotation system should be organised to ensure that foods are used in date order so are well within their keeping time. Care needs to be taken to ensure that all products are completely frozen when purchased and that they are not stored above the loading line in the cabinet.

Ready prepared frozen products carry a symbol which indicates the length of time the food can be safely stored.

Frozen foods should not be refrozen if they part-thaw as this can cause food poisoning. Great care must be taken to ensure that when frozen foods are transported from the supermarket they are packed in an insulated container to prevent them from thawing.

Some pieces of equipment enable foods to be frozen during manufacture. **Ice-cream makers** whip the mixture to distribute the frozen ice crystals and produce a thick creamy product.

Fig. 3.159 *An ice cream maker*

Finishing products

*Food products should always be attractively finished to make them appealing. A variety of colours and textures add a great deal of interest to dishes and make them more appetising. A **garnish** is the term used when savoury foods are attractively finished. A **decoration** is the term used when sweet foods are decoratively finished.*

Colour can be added to pastries by brushing on milk, beaten egg or egg yolk before they are cooked. The heat of the oven creates a golden brown finish which makes the finished product more attractive.

Foods can also be used to add colour to a finished product, e.g. using a bed of lettuce or watercress when serving sausage rolls or lasagne.

Fig. 3.160 *Food with an attractive garnish*

Fig. 3.161 *Doilies have been used to make food look more attractive*

Doilies can be used to create an attractive background for sweet products and **dishpapers** can be used for savoury products.

Texture can be added to sweet pastry products by brushing on egg white and dredging them with caster sugar. The heat of the oven cooks the egg white and melts the sugar to create a crystallised crusty finish.

Some foods can be **piped** onto products to create a more sophisticated result. Mashed potato, cream or butter icing can all be used in this way. Care needs to be taken that cream is not piped on too early as it can flop. Cream and butter icing should only be piped onto cold products or they will melt and spoil the finished appearance.

Decorations can indicate the flavours or fillings in a product. For example, a lemon cheesecake can be decorated with thin slices of lemon or finely grated lemon rind. A delicate orange-coloured butter icing can be used on an orange gateau.

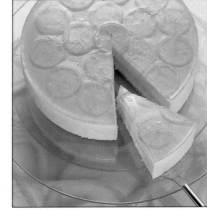

Fig. 3.162 *Lemon cheesecake*

Fig. 3.163 *This amount of green pepper provides the daily requirement of vitamin C for a teenager*

Some products can be decorated with foods which add valuable sources of nutrients. For example, pizzas can be topped with thin strips of green pepper, pieces of diced ham and slices of tomato. Together these create a colourful garnish but the green pepper is a valuable source of vitamin C so the quantity used may provide a large proportion of a teenager's daily requirements of this vitamin, while the ham provides protein and the tomato provides more vitamins.

4 PRODUCTS AND PRODUCT DESIGN

In industry products are designed and produced for sale in order to earn money and create wealth. Industrialised nations which do this successfully enjoy a high standard of living. The money that manufacturing industries earn helps to pay for service industries such as hospitals, housing and roads.

Manufacturing

People have designed and made food products since they first discovered cooking thousands of years ago. At first food products were made for personal use within the family unit , but soon people began to sell them or trade them for other goods. Gradually, as people began to work in factories, they moved away from the countryside. This made it difficult to grow and make their own food, particularly as most homes did not have gardens or ovens. People who were able to produce food in their own homes often did so to earn a living. These enterprises developed into cottage industries, producing small-scale batches of food products. The local baker and butcher are two examples of small-scale batch production.

Fig. 4.1
Shopping for milk then ...

The demand for convenience food products which come ready prepared, has grown significantly over the past 50 years due to social, economical and technological changes. The technological changes which have occurred in this period have allowed a greater number of food products to be produced on a large scale. The food industry is now the biggest single employer in the UK.

Fig. 4.2 *... and now*

Consumer pull and technology push

New products are often developed in response to demands made by consumers. Popular products already on the market are often studied as part of consumer research. Frequently this leads to new products being designed, e.g. low-fat versions of foods which are traditionally high in fat, such as biscuits. This is known as **consumer pull**. As long as consumers make demands for new or improved products, they will be designed to meet the consumers' requirements.

Products are also designed to make use of new technology. Old products are often redesigned or updated to enable technological developments to be used. Milk, for example, was once delivered in jugs. Pasteurised milk only became available once the technology was developed to allow pasteurisation to be carried out efficiently and cheaply. Yoghurt-style desserts, frozen pizzas, microwave meals and potato crisps have all been developed as technology has changed. This is known as **technology push**, when new technology 'pushes' forward the design of a product.

Developing a new product

These days new products are usually designed as a result of consumer pull or technology push. The following case study shows how one company identified an opportunity to produce a new range of products by targeting a particular section of the market.

Case study – MD Foods plc

Fig. 4.3

Fig. 4.4 *A selection of MD Foods' product range*

MD Foods plc is a part of a large worldwide dairy group. The company has many dairies throughout the UK, their headquarters being in Leeds, West Yorkshire. MD Foods produce many products, including Rosenborg cheeses, Pact reduced-fat spread and Southern Gold juices and drinks. They also produce the more familiar milk, cream and yoghurt products you might expect from a dairy. One of the best-known brands produced by MD Foods is Lurpak butter. You are probably familiar with Douglas the Butterman and his trombone.

Background

The market for flavoured milk drinks was growing and, like many dairy groups, MD Foods produced a flavoured milk drink, called Breaktime. However, Breaktime was not selling as well as products produced by MD Foods' competitors. MD Foods therefore decided that they needed to evaluate both their own product and also the products of their major competitors. This would enable them to **reformulate** their milk drink and gain an increased share of the market. This lead to the development of GULP!, the new flavoured milk drink produced by MD Foods.

Fig. 4.5 *Lurpak's Douglas the Butterman*

The design process

In industry professional designers do not always work in exactly the same way as you do in school. They usually develop a process which suits them and the particular product they are working on. In the food industry it is often necessary to begin designing by **evaluating** an existing product.

Evaluating in industry

During MD Foods' evaluation of their Breaktime drink, they identified an opportunity to design a new product range. This would allow them to attract new customers. In the food industry designers are often involved in reformulating existing products rather than creating new ones. Think of some 'new' products on the market. Can you see which products have been redesigned to create them? Changes to the design of products are made because of one or more of the problems shown in Fig. 4.6.

Market research

Market research involves collecting information from people, recording it and analysing it. It is carried out for several reasons:

- to discover the size of the demand for a product;
- to find out what will persuade people to buy or use a product;
- to evaluate how successful a product is.

- Falling sales;
- changing styles and fashions;
- the need to use new technology in the production process;
- the need to sell the product from a different angle (e.g. manufacturers may aim to produce a 'vegetarian' product to attract customers who are concerned about animal welfare);
- competition from rival products – manufacturers need to stay ahead of their competitors if they are to keep their share of the market (see page 27).

Fig. 4.6

Market research can be conducted in many ways, e. g. through the use of **questionnaires** and **face-to-face interviews**. Another method is to set up a **'focus group'**. This involves targeting an audience and inviting them to discuss the product you are researching. This is the method that MD Foods decided to use to research their new product range.

Their target audience was young people under 25 years of age. They were asked what they liked or disliked about the packaging of various drinks, and about the products themselves. The flavoured milk drinks were seen as boring, the packaging was dull and the foil tops used to close the bottles were not practical. When the tasters were asked to liken the drinks to a car, the milk drinks were generally seen to be like a Reliant Robin!

* Change the shape of bottle or carton
* Redesign the packaging – upbeat, jazzy, trendy
* Design a top that will open easily and can be used to reseal the drink
* Improve marketing to attract a younger market
* Promote healthy angle using a sports personality to promote the drink
* Alter the product itself

Fig. 4.7 *Marketing strategy*

After evaluating the results of their market research it was clear to MD Foods that there was a problem with the existing product. Their share of the market was falling, the competitors' products were selling better, and the product did not meet the needs of the consumer. A **project team** was set up to consider possible solutions to these problems (see Fig. 4.7). The decision was made to produce a new, flavoured milk drink. Not only that, it was also decided that a whole new approach to marketing the flavoured milk drink was needed. Fig. 4.8 shows the new brief given to the product and advertising designers.

At this stage in school you may be asked to **analyse** the situation, identify the **areas for research** and the ways in which you may conduct this research and then to complete a **specification** before you began designing the product and packaging. At MD Foods this part of the work had already been done because the process had begun with the evaluation of an existing product. At MD Foods the designers developed a **marketing strategy**.

Produce a flavoured milk product which is 'cool' and 'trendy' and will appeal to the youth market. Reassess the image, packaging and branding to produce a product based on sterilised milk which will enable flavoured milk to be seen as a soft drink. This new product should be able to compete with other soft drinks such as Tango and Irn Bru.

Fig. 4.8 *The design brief*

Marketing

Marketing is about making sure that people want to buy the product you are producing and that you are producing what people want to buy. There are four key points to marketing, often referred to as the '**4Ps**' (Fig. 4.9) Thinking of marketing in this way will help you to understand what is known as the '**marketing mix**'.

The competition

In producing the new flavoured drink MD Foods would be in direct competition with other manufacturers of flavoured milk drinks. They also aimed to compete with fizzy soft drink products. To be successful the product would have to appeal to the teenage market and meet the demand for a refreshing drink which teenagers would want to buy repeatedly.

Fig. 4.9 *The marketing mix*

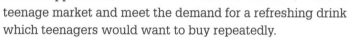

Fig. 4.10 *Rival products*

The product should be:

- creamy but not thick;
- a refreshing drink;
- produced in strawberry, chocolate and banana flavours (the three core flavours for milk drinks);
- sterilised to enable storage without chilling;
- exciting;
- in a re-sealable bottle.

Fig. 4.11 *Design specification checklist*

The marketing strategy

Instead of drawing up a detailed specification for the product, the design team developed a marketing strategy. The marketing strategy consisted of four main parts: **product**, **promotion**, **place** and **price**.

Product – The recipe of the existing product would be reformulated. The new flavoured milk drink would be different in taste and texture from the existing product. Following the market research, several criteria had been identified as being essential for the new product. These became part of the **design specification**.

The bottle shape and labelling would be made more exciting, showing the 'attitude' of drinks like Tango and Irn Bru. A screw top would be used to close the bottle, as demanded by the consumers in the tasting session.

Promotion – The target audience was to be the youth market. The product would be advertised in teen magazines and by using outdoor media such as buses.

Place – The new drink would be sold in the chilled cabinets of 'impulse' outlets, such as garages and newsagents, where people pick up drinks and snacks as they pay for petrol or buy newspapers. It would also be sold in supermarkets, to teenagers themselves and also to shoppers buying for

teenagers. The main difference here is the positioning of the product. In supermarkets, flavoured milks have traditionally been sold either next to the long life milks or from the chilled cabinet with other milk products. The aim of MD Foods was to have GULP! placed in the soft drinks area, alongside fizzy drinks and bottled mineral water. To allow this, the product would have to be based on sterilised or UHT milk as other types of milk require chilling to prevent spoilage. (Sterilised milk products were preferred to UHT products in the tasting session.)

Price – This would need to be comparable to the competitors' prices. The price of drinks in this area of the market was carefully monitored to ensure that the product was affordable. It was also important that the price represented 'value for money'.

The product

The process of converting raw materials into the product which has been designed is known as **manufacture**. GULP! is manufactured from a number of primary and secondary products, including fresh milk. From the processing plant in Newcastle, GULP! is transported around the world.

The main ingredient in GULP! is fresh milk supplied by herds of dairy cows on many farms around Britain. The milk is transported from the farms to the processing plant in modern milk tankers.

Fig. 4.13 *The modern milk tankers used by MD Foods*

Fig. 4.14 *Banana-flavoured GULP! coming off the production line*

On arrival at the processing plant the milk is **checked** to ensure that it is of the quality and safety demanded by the manufacturing specification. The ingredients are then **combined** in large tanks before being put into the bottles. Once filled, the bottles are **sealed** with a foil cap. The flavoured milk is then **sterilised**.

Sterilisation is a heat treatment which destroys all bacteria, ensuring that the milk will stay fresh and safe for long periods of time. During sterilisation the milk must be held at a temperature above 105°C for more than **20 minutes**. Once treated in this way the milk can be kept without refrigeration for up to six months. After opening, the milk must be treated as fresh milk and has to be stored in a refrigerator if it is not drunk straight away.

The shape of the GULP! bottle was designed to allow sterilisation to take place when the milk drink was already in the bottle. Each bottle has several ridges. These allow for the expansion and contraction which take place during heating and cooling.

After the sterilisation process a **date-coded plastic sleeve** is fastened on to the bottle. This is done by a machine which cuts the plastic strip and wraps it around the bottle. In the event of any problems with the product, this date code will allow the manufacturer to recall all suspect items and also to trace back to each supplier any ingredients which may have caused a problem.

The bottles then pass into a **heat tunnel** where the plastic shrinks to fit the shape of the bottle The screw cap is now added to the bottle.

At this point the bottles are **packed** into cases of ten and covered in shrink wrap to make handling and transportation easier. The cases then pass through quality control checks before being released for sale.

Fig. 4.15 *The product*

- on delivery the milk is checked for bacterial contamination
- mixed with flavourings
- bottles filled
- sealed with a foil cap
- sterilised
- the sleeve is wrapped around the bottle
- the sleeve is heat shrunk onto the bottle
- the sleeve is date coded
- the bottle is capped
- bottles are cased
- checked by quality control
- released for sale

Quality assurance

It is the responsibility of designers and manufacturers to ensure that their products are safe and will meet the high standards the customer expects. Food manufacturing faces special problems here as food which is incorrectly handled may cause illness or even death in the people who eat it. All food products must meet UK, EU and worldwide standards before they can be sold. As part of the **quality assurance** process food manufacturers must identify any stage in the production process where the food may be at risk. Tests of these stages must be planned before production begins. This is part of the process known as **HACCP** (**Hazard Analysis, Critical Control Point**). The tests which are carried out during and after manufacture are commonly known as **quality control**.

Quality control in industry

Quality control tests check the safety of the food and its fitness for the purpose for which it is to be sold. These tests are used to ensure that the product matches the specification in terms of flavour, texture and appearance.

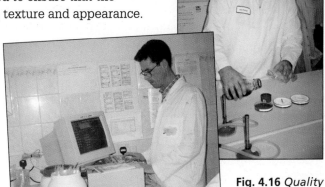

During the manufacture of GULP! several quality control tests will be carried out. These include testing the **temperature** of the milk when it arrives at the processing plant. It must be below 5°C if it is to be accepted. **Microbiological tests** check the bacteria level in the milk, which would affect the drinking or keeping qualities of the finished product. The **ingredients** used in making the flavoured milk will be tested when they arrive to check that the containers have not been opened and that they are still within the 'use by' date mark.

Fig. 4.16 *Quality control tests*

During manufacture the milk will be tested to ensure that the high temperatures needed for **sterilisation** are reached. After manufacturing samples will be taken and stored to ensure that the milk has been sterilised correctly and will keep for long periods without developing 'off' flavours. **Sensory testing** will also be carried out to make sure that the product is of the high standard of taste, texture and appearance planned by the designers.

Fig. 4.17
Cardboard and glass packaging

Packaging

The packaging of any product is important as it has a number of functions to fulfil. First, it must **protect** the food. Only certain types of materials can be used for food items. The range of materials which could have been used include **cardboard**, **plastic**, **cans** and **glass**. Plastic was chosen as it is lightweight, can be heated during sterilisation, and is flexible and practical.

Second, packaging is the first line of communication between the consumer and the manufacturer. Any **information** which the manufacturer wants or needs to pass to the consumer can be put on the label on the packaging. Some of this information is a legal requirement, while other items, e.g. the **bar code**, are needed by the retailer. Some information is given to allow the manufacturer to build up a databank of details about the consumers who purchase their product. This is often done by using a '**customer care line**'.

Fig. 4.18

Packaging can also communicate information about a product through its shape, colour and style of lettering. Look at Fig. 4.18. How are colour combinations and lettering used in these items? What can you tell about the target group of each product from the packaging that has been used?

The MD Foods designers were required to produce a package which would give a new image to the flavoured milk drink and encourage young people to buy it. When designing the packaging for GULP! different colour combinations and styles were modelled using a computer. This is a quick way of considering a variety of combinations, shapes and letters without going to the expense of making 3D models. The eye-catching colour combinations, bright lettering and curvy bottle all form part of the promotion of the product.

The following information may be found on labels.

- **Weight** – legally required on most products, exceptions include bread under 300 g, standard loaves and any product under 25 g.
- **Name and address of manufacturer** – this may be printed on the packet if the food is imported.
- **Cooking instructions** – must be on packets if the food needs cooking.
- **Storage instructions** – must be on a packet if the food would become harmful through being stored incorrectly.
- **Name of the product** – unless the product can be seen through the wrapper.
- **Description of the product** – only needed if the food cannot be identified by its name.

Fig. 4.19
The chosen design

- **'Best before'** date for products with a long shelf-life or **'use by'** date for short shelf-life products.
- **Country of origin** – if there may be some confusion, e.g. an Italian pizza which is actually made in Germany.
- **List of ingredients** – these may be omitted if the package is too small to accommodate them, or if the product is part of a 'multi-pack', such as ice-cream cornets sold in packs of four. The ingredients will be listed on the outer wrapper but do not have to be found on individual wrappers.
- **Other information** – this is included at the manufacturer's discretion but may include bar codes, money-off coupons, etc.

Promotion

This term is used to describe any activity which brings the product to the notice of consumers and encourages them to purchase the product. A wide range of activities are carried out as part of promotion.

The team responsible for promoting GULP! considered all the areas which would appeal to the youth market. They decided that any advertising campaign needed to be bold and humorous. The first activity was to decide on a name for the new product. At a team meeting a **brainstorming session** was used, based on words associated with drinking. Words like 'slurp', 'quench' and 'swallow' were considered, but GULP! was considered to be the best.

Fig. 4.20 *Promotional activities*

Fig. 4.21

The advertisements designed for teenage magazines were all based on a play on the word GULP! Situations which would make anyone go GULP! were used. These were made into fun cartoons (you can see some of them in Fig. 4.21).

The advertisements can be seen on the side of all M.D. Foods lorries. A memorable slogan was needed which would appeal to young people. Again, this was based on the word GULP! – 'Don't swallow – GULP!'

Press releases were issued to marketing magazines like *The Grocer*. This brought the product to the attention of retailers. **Free-trial, money-off coupons** appeared in local newspapers. These were aimed in particular at the parents of children.

Fig. 4.22 *Over the first year of the new product's life MD Foods intend to spend £1.2 million pounds on promoting it*

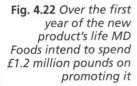

Advertisements appeared in both teenage and women's magazines, using different photographs to appeal to the different age groups.

Fig. 4.24 *The first three flavours produced*

Fig. 4.23 *Promotional photos were intended to appeal to both parents and teenagers*

Future developments

The three flavours originally manufactured were strawberry, banana and chocolate. These three were chosen because in the market research carried out among young people they were shown to be the most popular flavours.

Plans to expand the product range in the future include thick shakes and a high energy version, to be known as GULP! GTI. This will be sold alongside other sports drinks like Red Bull or Energise! A wider range of flavours may also be developed, including 'seasonal' special flavours for Christmas, Easter or summer.

GULP! has proved to be hugely successful so far. In a competition (a little like the Oscars for food and drink) Gulp! won the 'best new product' award for soft drinks.

Fig. 4.25 *In 1989 GULP! won the 'best new product' award for soft drinks*

ACKNOWLEDGEMENTS

The publishers would like to thank the following for their help in researching and providing material:

    Debbie Powell at MD Foods plc

    Kathy Wheeler at Fiskars

    Helen Griffiths at Hughes

    Martin Sookias

    Meat and Livestock Commission

    Mel Hughes at Commotion

    Peter Jurgensen at Lego

Beamish Open Air Museum (4.1)

Anthony Blake Photo Library (1.14, 1.66, 2.3, 2.8, 2.25, 2.27, 2.28, 3.2, 3.20, 3.21, 3.22, 3.32, 3.43 3.58, 3.60, 3.55, 3.70, 3.77, 3.80, 3.84, 3.85, 3.97, 3.101, 3.104, 3.106, 3.108, 3.109, 3.111, 3.112, 3.113, 3.114, 3.115, 3.116, 3.117, 3.124, 3.125, 3.126, 3.127, 3.128, 3.129, 3.130, 3.133, 3.140, 3.142, 3.143, 3.144, 3.147, 3.149, 3.151, 3.160, 3.162, 3.163)

British Sugar (2.30, 3.57)

Delonghi (3.159)

Fiskars (Kitchen Devils) (3.118, 3.119, 3.120, 3.121, 3.122, 3.123)

Food Features (2.17, 3.63, 3.71, 3.74, 3.82, 3.88, 3.98, 3.100, 3.110, 3.145, 3.148, 3.161)

Janet Inglis (1.6, 1.50, 1.57, 1.58, 4.16)

Kenwood (3.136)

Andrew Lambert (3.56)

Lego (1.39)

Alexis Maryon (3.7, 3.17)

MD Foods plc (4.3, 4.4, 4.5, 4.13, 4.14, 4.19, 4.21, 4.22, 4.23, 4.24, 4.25)

Meat and Livestock Commission (2.10, 3.18, 3.96)

Angus Mill (3.13)

Morphy Richards (3.3, 3.139)

Moulinex (3.137)

Sue Plews (3.24, 3.25, 3.59, 3.65, 3.66, 3.68, 3.69, 3.77, 3.78, 3.79, 3.80, 3.81, 3.86, 3.89, 3.90, 3.91, 3.92, 3.132)

RSPCA (2.11, 2.12)

Russell Hobbs (3.139, 3.150)

Safeway (2.15, 4.2)

Science Photo Library (3.30)

Martin Sookias (1.5, 1.13, 1.32, 1.63, 1.65, 2.2, 2.9, 2.14, 2.20, 2.22, 2.23, 2.24, 2.31, 2.32, 2.34, 2.36, 3.1, 3.10, 3.11, 3.28, 3.31, 3.34, 3.35, 3.36, 3.37, 3.38, 3.39, 3.40, 3.42, 3.50, 3.51, 3.52, 3.57, 3.61, 3.62, 3.64, 3.69, 3.75, 3.93, 4.10, 4.18)

Southwark Trading Standards (3.6)

Tefal (3.99, 3.139, 3.146)

The Stock Market (1.9, 1.10)

Tony Stone Images (1.7, 1.34, 2.1, 2.26)

Walls (3.83)

Warrens (3.102)

Figs 1.42 and 1.43 have been developed from original work by Jenny Ridgewell published in Tasting and Testing (1993, Ridgwell Press).

Every effort has been made to contact the holders of copyright material, but if any have been inadvertently overlooked, the Publishers will be pleased to make the necessary arrangements at the first opportunity.

Note to teachers

Collins Food Foundation Course *has been written to suit National Curriculum Food Technology at Key Stage 3. Following the hugely successful* Collins Design and Technology Foundation Course. *It includes up-to-date material on skills and processes used in the food industry. An in-depth case study of real-life new products from concept to manufacture enhances pupils understanding of the designing and making process.*

Throughout the book you will find questions related to the material on the page, and safety issues are highlighted wherever they are relevant.

Be aware of safety. Look for the symbol:

This book provides a solid foundation for GCSE Food Technology, as well as GNVQ Manufacturing.

Other titles in the series are: *Collins Design and Technology Foundation Course* and *Collins Textiles Foundation Course.*

Build on the success of work in Collins Food Foundation Course with Food Technology. Part of the highly acclaimed Collins Real-World Technology series the book is written to support GCSE Food Technology and GNVQ Manufacturing.

Containing a wide variety of case studies, Food Technology provides an invaluable perspective on the food industry and an understanding of industrial practices.

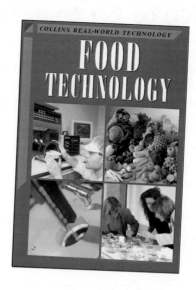

- Offers comprehensive coverage of all the necessary knowledge and skills to design and make quality food products.

- Covers systems and control, processing techniques, nutrition, product development, quality assurance and packaging.

- Up-to-date information on 'future foods' and biotechnology.

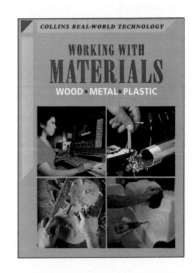

- Features two in-depth case studies of new food products.

Food Technology *'Covers the important aspects of food technology... up-to-date facts and excellent case study materials'* TES

Further books in Collins Real World Technology series include Working With Materials, Communicating Design and Electronic Products. These books provide the complete requirements for GCSE and Standard Grade qualifications.

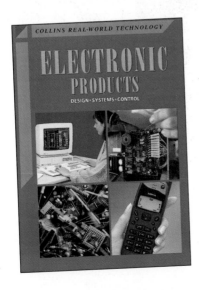

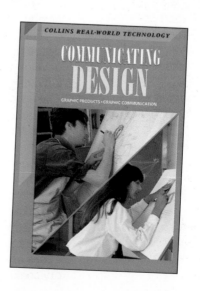

INDEX